# GROWING DOWN

CONFINGO PUBLISHING

# GROWING DOWN

GRAHAM WILSON

First published in the UK in 2022 by Confingo Publishing
249 Burton Road, Didsbury, Manchester M20 2WA

www.confingopublishing.uk

Cover image by Olivia Boileau

Typesetting by John Oakey

Printed by TJ Books Limited

A CIP catalogue record for this book is available from the British Library

ISBN 978-1-7399614-5-9

2 4 6 8 10 9 7 5 3 1

And one man in his time plays many parts

*As You Like It, II, vii*

## PROLOGUE

A passing ARP warden would have been more than curious. Why should any man, at such an unearthly hour, be turning over his potato patch? What possible culinary need could have driven him into his garden on such a bitter March night? But no such warden was passing, nor was the man digging for victory. For it wasn't potatoes the man was after, but petrol, or more precisely a can containing petrol, that he had buried several months earlier. Generally speaking, the digger was a law-abiding man and fully aware that the storage of fuel during this current emergency was illegal. But he was also a practical man who knew, although he'd never admit it, that right and wrong, whatever the poet might say, were not absolutes.

It hadn't been long after the outbreak of war that his wife had discovered she was pregnant and he had known, or at least guessed, that in six or seven months' time, when the bombing might be more fierce and even more frightening, he would have to act not only quickly but calmly. Then he had buried the can and prayed that its contents would not totally evaporate.

Now, with increasing ferocity, he first loosened then excavated sufficient soil to reveal the slightly rusted edge of the container. Abandoning the spade, he scrabbled with both hands until with a final heave he managed to wrench the can from its hiding place and part carry, part drag his newly acquired baggage towards the house. It was reassuringly heavy. Removing his gloves, he twisted the cap and emptied the contents into the tank of his car. He stopped and thought carefully. Was there anything he had missed? Once started, there'd be no time to go back. ID card. Letter from Dr Thompson. The blinds on the headlights fitted weeks earlier. Almost ready to go. He reached under the driver's seat for the starting handle. A moment of panic, but of course it was there, exactly where he had put it. At the third swing, the cylinders moved, then moved again of their own volition until the shuddering vibrations eventually settled into a regular mechanical rhythm. He eased the car on to the drive where his wife stood clutching a small suitcase. After he had half coaxed, half bundled her on to the back seat, he stood for a moment and looked up at the sky. Yes, it will suit them tonight. He'll have to be quick.

It started, as it always started, with the undulating moan of the air-raid siren. Then nothing except perhaps a burst of fire from a trigger-happy ack-ack shooting at shadows. But you knew what was coming. The sound, at first sufficiently faint to encourage the hope that, tonight, they are after some other target, but then as the drone grows louder and nearer you know, yet again, they were after the docks. In an ever-building crescendo, that tired old expression 'all hell broke loose' loses its glib familiarity among the cacophony of splintering glass, tumbling masonry, shrieking whistles, voices frantically raised and the ever-increasing agonised screams.

Yet among this carnage the maternity ward of City General hospital was the calm eye of the storm. Sister O'Driscoll carefully arranging what had to be arranged, reassuring when reassurance was needed. Thinking what a terrible hullaballoo to be happening on the day of her country's patron saint. Eventually the clamour started to lessen. The light from the few remaining explosions was no longer able to pierce the blackout that covered the windows. The screams turned to moans, and moans to silence. Sister O'Driscoll looked down at the watch pinned to her uniform. A quarter to twelve.

'If it should be a son you'll be having, will you be after calling him Patrick?'

The mother-to-be, who had strong sectarian views in this most sectarian of cities, said nothing. Just tightened her lips and stared fixedly at a point on the ceiling. Midnight came and went. Outside, the roof of a house that could no longer defy gravity slid to the ground. Then, at last, the continuous almost defiant note of the all-clear which, in turn, gave way to the petulant cry of new-born life. Sister O'Driscoll picked up what looked little more than a bundle of clothing and smiled one of her most reassuring of smiles.

'Merciful Mother of God. It's a boy.'

## PANTOMIME

How did the storybook go? For the want of a nail a shoe was lost. For the want of the shoe a horse was lost. For the want of a horse a battle... I suppose to lose a battle is really important but probably not as important as losing your soul.

Best not think of losing my soul. Try to think of something else. For a start if I keep my face very close to the window, no one'll know I'm singing to myself and I can try to remember the words of that song. It's dark outside the warmth of the tram. Puddles catch the pale yellowy reflections of the street lamps and I can see passers-by, collars up to keep warm, move along in a hurried shuffle. What were the words? *I'll be yours forever.* Forever is a long time away. At least I hope so. Forever. That's a word that gives me a bit of bother nowadays. Squashing my nose against the glass, I try out the tune. In the reflection I can see Aunt Helen with my little brother and, behind them, both my parents, and hear Mother talking above the general hubbub. *You'd think they'd find a female lead who could sing. She couldn't hold a note if you gave her a basket. And why they don't do a decent Gilbert and Sullivan, I'll never understand. It's all very well beating Hitler...* 'Rosalind, I'll be yours forever.' That's what the hunter said or rather sang and I'd begun to hope that I could be too.

The tram seems to have suddenly filled up. So many faces. I wonder how you can tell if someone has lost their soul? It can't be that obvious. I mean not like in Africa where there are hundreds of thousands of lost souls. Souls as black as their poor little bodies, is what Aunt Helen says. I mean if I *have* lost my soul, I suppose in the end I'm bound to start turning black like the poor little Africans. Perhaps it has started already. Better check my reflection again. No, not much sign yet. The question is where would the blackening begin? Probably at the tip of my nose and then spread across my face down my neck across my chest until it entirely filled up my whole body inside and out. There again, it might start with the little toe of one of my feet and you can't very well start taking your shoes and socks off on a tram in front of all these people, can you?

Do horses have toes? I'll have to check in that book in Father's library. At least, that's what he calls it. Mother says it's not a library at all, just a room with a lot of books no one ever reads. For once, I agree with her. It's nothing like a library. In a library you have to keep very, very quiet. I once heard my father answer the telephone in his library and talk quite loudly and even begin laughing. I'm sure the library lady wouldn't have allowed that. You can't even whisper, let alone laugh. In my father's library I like to pull the books off the shelves. At least those I can reach. The big heavy ones are the best. You have to really struggle to get them off but once on the carpet you can open them up and turn over the pages. Very slowly like opening a Christmas present. I don't understand them much but there is one storybook I really like. It is quite old and the edges of the pages are made of gold and when you open the front there is some writing that says *To Jack from Granny Nelson*. I don't know who Granny Nelson is but I think Jack must be my father as Mother sometimes calls him that. On one side of the page is a sort of poem and on the other side a picture that shows what the poem is really about. I like the pictures best, particularly the one with the soldier and his horse. The soldier looks very angry and the horse very sad. But the bit I like best is the guns in the background firing. Great splodges of smoke and red and yellow flashes of fire.

For the loss of a horse... Do horses have souls? They must have or they wouldn't go to heaven. Mrs O'Laughlin at Sunday School said all animals go to heaven and started to talk about her dear little puppies. That was when Billy Thompson started. *Even rats?* Mrs O'Laughlin was not sure about rats. *I've got a white rat. Did Baby Jesus keep rats?* Mrs O'Laughlin said she couldn't be certain but probably not. I wonder if Rosalind will go to heaven. I expect so. She's much prettier than the angels in the nativity play. In fact, they weren't pretty at all just good at bossing people about, but I expect angels have to be pretty good at doing that. Better check the window again. Still no sign of going black.

Now Mother's given up talking about the singing and has moved on to how it isn't like it was before the war when going to the theatre was a real occasion. I'd never been in a proper theatre before. Not like the one we'd just been to. There was a stage at school of course when we did the nativity play. We'd had what Miss Marshall called auditions to see who would play what part. I wanted to play Joseph as he had the most words and I was sure Barbara Fannage would get the part of Mary as everyone likes Barbara. But as expected Edward Yeales got the vote and I had to put up with being a shepherd. I didn't mind being a shepherd really as I quite like sheep. More than cows anyway. We once went to the farm at the top of the road and the yard was full of cows making an awful noise. The farmer was trying to get them back into the field when one black and white one with big horns came charging towards us. It was all right though as we could get back through the gate and on to the road. Anyway, Billy Thompson was also chosen as a shepherd so that meant it wasn't too bad. Of course it would have been better if we had had real sheep rather than stupid cardboard boxes with rugs stuck on top of them.

But being at the proper theatre was different. I have to say that it was not only different but the best thing that had ever happened to me in my life. Even better than when Billy and me found the red and silver sticklebacks in the stream that runs past the bottom of his garden. First the whole place went slowly dark as if someone was very slowly drawing the curtains over the window which was odd really as what was really happening was the curtains in front of the stage were being very slowly opened. At first all you could see were the black shapes of trees against a purply sky and then the sky changed from purple to orange then yellow and in the end a sort of blue colour. As these colours changed you could see more and more of the scene until at last Rosalind seemed to appear out of the gloom sitting half in and half out of the doorway of a hut stirring a pot which was steaming away on a wood fire. Of course, I didn't know her name was Rosalind then. She was just a lady with long dark hair stirring a pot and singing a song. A light slowly lit up her face and the music started playing. I don't think I've ever seen anything so special in my life. It's very hard to describe how I felt. Sort of happy and sad at the same time. It was all a bit like magic as if I was in a story in a story book until I was told to sit up properly in my seat and stop fidgeting.

It was a bit like that other special event that was almost as special as Christmas itself. When Father unlocked the cupboard under the stairs and brought out the stepladders as Mother said for their annual airing and how he never did things around the house like painting the walls and ceilings and hanging up pictures. Then there was a bit of a fuss and Father would say each to his own you should never do a tradesman out of a job and the fuss would stop. We then all went upstairs Father Mother Aunt Helen my little brother and me. Father very carefully pulled the legs of the ladder apart and then even more carefully climbed the first few rungs. Once he could reach the ceiling he pushed back a trapdoor and climbed up another couple of steps. First his head and then his arms and shoulders disappeared and when he spoke his voice was all muffled. Then he started passing things down out of the loft to Aunt Helen and when he had finished we all gathered round to make sure nothing was missing. As well as the tinsel and ribbons there were the four large cardboard boxes. My brother and I are allowed to carry the tinsel and ribbons downstairs but Father and Aunt Helen carried the boxes between them. Once downstairs they are laid in a row on the settee and the lids carefully removed.

*Now boys you can look but don't touch.*

In the first box were twelve silver and red candleholders that clipped on to the branches of the Christmas tree and in a separate section twelve little red candles. In the second box different-coloured balls each with its own gold-wire loop fixed to the top. But it was the opening of the third that I was really waiting for. The box was divided into nine different compartments and each one contained a different fruit covered in silver paper and made so Aunt Helen says out of chocolate. As you'd expect there was an apple, a pear and a plum but the one I really liked was the peach. I'd never seen a real peach or tasted chocolate for that matter. Aunt Helen says it's because of the war. It's also because of the war Aunt Helen lives with us. The war's stopped now so I don't know why she's still living with us. Perhaps because there's going to be another war and she thought she may as well stop as go away and come back again. You can never tell with grown-ups. Finally, there was the star which had a box all to itself which Aunt Helen said was very right and proper whatever that means. It was always at this point that Mother finally took charge.

*Don't touch, boys! You heard what your father said. Aunt Helen will decorate the tree.*

It's funny how some things just happen and then how one thing just leads to another. I'd been sent to the front room because the vet had come to see Robbie who was lying on the dining-room floor keeping warm in front of the gas fire. I could hear the vet Mr Pallister talking to Father. I could tell he was trying to keep his voice down so I couldn't hear. Anyway I had nothing to do except wait so I thought I'd have a proper look at the ornaments on the Christmas tree. As I've said, the one I really like is the peach. What I really wanted to do was take it off its branch and have a proper look at it, but I couldn't quite reach to do that. So I thought I would just touch it to see what it felt like and whether it was as furry as it looked. I could just reach to touch it if I stood on tiptoe and I suppose it was then when it must have happened. As I reached up I must have bumped into another bit of the tree and the next thing I knew the apple which had been on one of the lower branches was lying on the floor. I knew without looking it would be broken. Of course I also knew that would mean trouble and sure enough that's when all this bother about losing my soul and turning black began.

Now that the tram's passing the end of Oswald Street I can just see if I look carefully the end bit of our school. Christmas is over so it's back tomorrow. I quite like going to school but I like going home better. Not because I *like* home better than school. At school I seem to do the reading and sums and stuff more easily than most of the others so the teacher leaves me alone and shouts at Billy Thompson instead. So school's all right most of the time. No it is the actual *going* home that I like. The best part is there are two sorts of going home – dinner-time going home and teatime going home. The last lesson before dinner is reading to Miss Marshall from the *Early Learning* book. We all have to get to a certain part and then we can go home. Me and Barbara Fannage nearly always finish first and as we live the same way we set off together. Once we've crossed the main road at the traffic lights she'll give me a punch on the arm and say *Race you to the corner* and off she'd go. No matter how hard I try she always beats me. She can run like the wind and be easily first to the corner where she stops and waits for me to catch up. As soon as I get there she straight away runs round the corner and up to the gate of her house – the one with a dustbin outside. There she stops looks round and before going in sticks her tongue out which I'm sure is not the sort of thing Mary the Mother of Jesus should do.

I quite like Barbara Fannage but she's not my real friend. My real friend is Billy Thompson. It is going home with him at teatime that I really like. On the way home we always stop to play in the woods. Billy and me try to climb the trees and he shows me where the bears live at night-time. I said there weren't any bears in England but he said I didn't know what I was talking about and his Uncle Joe who went into the woods lots of times at night had told him he'd seen them so there. I wasn't supposed to play with Billy. Aunt Helen says Mother doesn't approve of him. *They could at least call him William or even Bill. Billy is such a common name.* I tried calling him William once. We were throwing sticks at a horse chestnut tree trying to get conkers. He just sort of stopped with the stick in his hand and for a moment I thought he was going to throw it at me but he just threw it at a bush and said he had to go home. I don't blame him. I don't think I'd want to be called William. It sounds somehow sort of serious and not much fun. Now Billy's a great name. I wouldn't mind being called Billy. Next day I thought perhaps he wouldn't want to play in the woods any more but he seemed all right about it after I showed him some bear prints I'd found.

The funny thing was there was a bear in Rosalind's play as well. It happened just after the interval. You couldn't see much but you could hear the curtains slowly opening and all around the stage was a pinkish red glow. Then very very slowly the darkness around the glow got lighter and lighter and as there was more and more light you could start to see the shapes of trees and bushes. Then there was a strange shape moving behind the trees and one or two of the other children watching started to shout out. I could feel Mother was looking at me in case I shouted out. But I wouldn't have. It was more important than that. Then some hunters dressed in green came in and asked Rosalind if she had seen a bear roaming around the neighbourhood and if she did see it she was to tell them at once as it was very dangerous and might eat her up.

Most of the rest of the story was about the bear coming on the stage and just missing people he could eat up. Whenever the bear appeared the man playing the drums played them really loud and the lights on the stage changed to very dark red. The bear nearly caught Rosalind once but she ran away. Even though she could run like the wind the bear was even faster and just when I thought the bear was going to catch Rosalind a hunter carrying a gun came in and rescued her. And then there was lots of singing that didn't seem to mean anything and a clown who was quite funny when he tried to hide from the bear and in the end all the hunters surrounded the bear and the head hunter shot it. Then all the people from the village came on stage and they all seemed very happy so they all sang another song and the curtains closed. Then all the lights in the theatre came on and people started talking and pushing and shoving to get out. For some reason that made me feel quite sad but not sad like last time.

*Come on don't dawdle or we'll miss the last tram.*

It wasn't as though I'd actually broken it. I mean the silver paper was already torn and hanging off the apple. All I'd done after I'd picked it up off the floor was to peel it back a bit to see what was inside. And that was when the bit of chocolate seemed to break off. I had really tried to put it back together but it wouldn't stick, so I thought I may as well eat the broken bit – now the war is finished. Aunt Helen also says waste not want not. I am not sure what that means but it's something to do with eating cabbage and some poor little Indians. I heard Mr Pallister talking in the hall so I called out to ask him if Robbie would be all right. He said he expected so but I knew he didn't really mean it. Then I put the broken apple back on the Christmas tree anyway.

It's still raining outside the tram but there aren't many

people walking along the pavement any more. That means we must be getting near to the terminus where we get off. I've given up checking my nose in the windows. When it's dark outside you can't see properly if your face is turning black anyway. I've decided it's probably better to think about Rosalind and the hunters. It must have been while I was thinking about Rosalind that I decided that I no longer wanted to be a tram conductor when I grew up. What I had liked about that job was that as the tram can't turn around when it gets to the terminus the driver has to get out and get in the other end and the conductor has to walk down the aisle, first upstairs and then downstairs with his arms stretched out to each side and with his hand clatter the backs of the seats so they face the other way. I'd still like to be able to clatter the seats but now I've decided I want to be a hunter and help kill all the bears instead.

It's not far from the tram stop to where we live and as my brother opens the front gate I notice the curtains have been left open and the street light outside our house catching the gold-wire loop of a pink-coloured ball. I couldn't see the apple but I knew it would be on the table where she put it with that other book – the one I didn't want to think about – lying where it had fallen with such a terrible thud. I couldn't see much else but I knew the rest would be just like it was when my little brother couldn't stop crying.

I suppose remembering his face brought it all back to me. How it had all started – this thing about losing my soul and if actually not touching it meant it didn't count. You could say it really started when Mr Pattison had stopped at the front door and was still talking to Father so I couldn't get into the library and after wandering around the kitchen for a bit I was on my way to the dining room to have a look at

Robbie when I heard Mother call out in a very sharp voice.

'Come in here, young man.'

I went back into the lounge to see her with my little brother who looked as though he was about to burst into tears. I then saw the chocolate apple no longer on the tree but lying forlornly in the centre of the table we never use unless we're having people to tea. There was little or no beating about the bush as Aunt Helen would say.

'Are you responsible for this?'

*Responsible for what?* seemed the best answer under the circumstances. 'Don't be stupid. This.' She pointed at the apple, its silver paper peeled even further back to show the broken chocolate.

I shook my head. If I'd only had a chance to explain. Of course I had done it but I mean I wasn't really to blame. It had just fallen off. It wasn't my fault it broke. It was probably really old anyway. So I just said nothing. I could see she was a bit stuck by that. She looked at my brother and then back at me.

*Are you sure you didn't touch this, darling?*

My little brother looked at me then back to his mother eyes wide open.

*Of course you didn't. You wouldn't be able to reach.*

For the want of a nail a shoe was lost. For the want of a shoe a horse was lost. For the want of horse... Now all for the want of a lie a soul was lost. He could easily have told her a bit of a lie – I mean, that's what little brothers are for.

She turned back to me. 'I'll ask you again. Did you' – pointing at the table – 'break this apple?'

'No.'

There was a moment of hesitation then she tightened her lips like she does when Aunt Helen doesn't agree with her. 'Very well.' She left the room and returned with a big book in her hand. 'We'll settle this once and for all.'

For a moment because of the gold edging I thought it was the book with the soldier and the horse but then I realised it was the wrong colour and much thicker.

'Now you know what this is.' It wasn't a question. 'It's the Bible, the Holy Bible.' I thought it best to nod. 'Now I want you to place your right hand on here.' She nodded at the book that she had thrust before me as if she was offering a present. It must have been pretty heavy because when I put my hand on the leather cover I could feel her arms shaking under the weight.

'I want you to swear on this Bible that you did not steal the piece of chocolate. Do you understand?' I nodded. 'And do you understand what will happen if you lie?' I nodded again. 'If you swear to God with your hand on the Holy Bible and lie that means when you die your soul will go to hell – forever. Now think carefully. Did you steal that bit of chocolate from the Christmas tree?'

I looked her straight in the eyes. She stared back. 'Did you?' Trying to make sure she kept looking at me I very slowly and ever so slightly lifted my hand off the book until I could feel the dampness separate itself from the leather cover. 'Did you?'

'No, definitely not.'

This seemed to take the wind out of her sails, as Aunt Helen would say, and for a moment or two she didn't seem to know what to do then with a rather funny noise she half dropped the book on to the table very close to the chocolate apple which rattled a bit. 'Then if it wasn't you, it *must* have been your brother. Was it you, darling?' She turned to my brother who I could see was about to start blubbering. 'Never mind, darling. I'm sure you didn't mean it. It must have been an accident.'

Last one in I carefully dropped the latch on the garden gate. Father as usual made a great fuss about finding the right key and putting it in the lock. At last the door opened and we all trooped in. *Now then. One two three four. Good we haven't lost anyone. Come in quick and shut the door to keep the cold out.* For some reason Father seemed very pleased with himself.

## THE LANCASTER BOMBER

*Of course, it had to be an accident.* Standing outside the lounge door, I can hear Mother on the phone, her voice quieter than it usually is. Always a bad sign. *No, no. I'll be all right. But, whatever happens, we mustn't* – I didn't hear the rest of the sentence as it was cut off by a gently closed door. That would be Aunt Helen, always the soul of discretion, as Father says. There was nothing much I could do except go to my bedroom and sit on the edge of the bed and wait.

As bedrooms go, it is a pretty decent one. At least I didn't have to share it with my little brother. His name is Paul and as I've just learnt from Latin, which I've just started at school, Paul means 'little' and that is probably fair enough as he is little, at least little compared to me as I'm four years older and as everyone keeps saying should know better. If he had been a bit older and I suppose a bit bigger or a bit taller everything might have been all right. He might even have gone to the fair instead of... instead of what happened. As Mother was trying to explain, it had to be an accident, but I knew deep down that it was really my fault no matter what Mother said on the telephone. After all it was me who decided.

As I said, as bedrooms go, mine was OK. It wasn't so much for the view, as Aunt Helen says, but because it had a big table under the window which had been put there so I could do my homework in peace and quiet. Why I liked it wasn't because I liked homework but because it was a really good space to build things on. And just now I was putting together the kit of a Lancaster Bomber which I'd got for my birthday. It came in a really long box with a picture in colour of the plane and across the top were the words 'THE LANCASTER BOMBER *Scourge of Nazi Germany*'. I'm not sure what scourge means but it sounds pretty scary like John Wayne in the film *Sands of Iwo Jima* which me and Mike have just seen except that was the Japanese not the Germans. Most of the other boys would have chosen Spitfires or Hurricanes. What I liked about this kit was it was not like Airfix models which, when all is said and done, were just lumps of wood with transfers stuck on them.

The kit of the Lancaster Bomber was much more complicated. You had to press out all the bits from the master sheet and follow the instructions very carefully to build up a framework of spars and stringers that looked pretty fragile by themselves but were really strong when glued together and covered with dope-treated tissue paper. Something about opposing forces or suchlike. Mike who is cleverer than me tried to explain it but I hadn't understood properly. But that wasn't the only reason why I chose it. What I want to be when I grow up is a proper cricketer and be famous like Don Bradman but I don't want to be a batsman, though I wouldn't mind scoring a century, but what I want to be is a fast bowler and the best fast bowler in the world's got a nickname, the 'Lancaster Bomber'. He's called that, Father says, because he lives in Lancashire and causes as much havoc as the planes did to the Germans in the war.

I remembered thinking I had timed it just right. There was just one thing left to do. Getting the last bit of the fuselage glued together so I'd be in time to join Mike and the rest. I'd tried very hard not to rush and spoil everything. It seems a long time ago now. And, of course, all this needn't have happened, if she'd allowed me to go when I wanted. But, as usual, it was all down to what she called values, like in that poem by Rudyard Kipling that the vicar keeps going on about. Things like keeping your word, turning up on time, and giving up your seat on the bus.

It was when I was walking downstairs that what happened actually began.

'Right, I'm going. Back for eight o'clock.'

Mother appeared out of the lounge. 'Where are you off to now?'

'I've told you. Off to the fair with Mike and Charlie.'

'I do wish you would call your friends by their proper names. I know their mothers are not at all happy about it.'

'Everyone calls them that.'

'Well, you are not everyone and their mothers certainly don't.'

'All right then. I'm off to the fair with Michael and Charles.' I deliberately dragged out each part of their names. Mother seemed to be about to reply when her attention was distracted by Paul, who had appeared behind her tugging her hand and saying something I couldn't quite catch.

'What did you say, darling?' Paul, twisting his fingers round his mother's, spoke this time a bit more clearly.

'But he did, he said he would play.' Mother looked from Paul to me. I dropped my hand from the door handle knowing full well what was coming next. The ace card that never failed. 'But he did. He promised.'

'Paul said you promised. Did you promise?' I tried to catch Paul's eye hoping he would realise some deal could be done if he changed his mind. He didn't even look at me, instead disappeared into the cupboard under the stairs to emerge dragging a bat two sizes too big for him. I knew I had lost, nevertheless felt I had to make some sort of effort. 'But I told Mike – Michael – and Charles I would go to the fair and I've got to catch the bus.' I shouldn't have said 'got to'. That was a mistake.

'Got to? What do you mean, "got to"? How many times do I have to tell you, you can't just do whatever you want? There are other people that must be considered.' Mother now really got going. 'What's more, I'm sure neither Michael nor Charles would promise their brothers something, then wander off on some frolic of their own. When you make a promise, you keep a promise. Do you understand?' I considered pointing out that Mike didn't have a brother, but decided against it. 'S'pose so. But I only promised one game.'

We always played on the outfield of the local cricket ground. We were not members and were not supposed to play there at all but Tom, the groundsman, was OK about it. As long as we did no damage, he turned a blind eye. Would even cut a wicket for us, if he was not too busy. Not at the pavilion end, mind, but alongside the sight screen that blocked most of the view from the non-members' grandstand. He was all right, Tom, better than some adults I could mention. I walked ahead towards the lane that led to the loose plank in the fence. After I was out of sight of the house I deliberately lengthened my stride, making Paul, struggling with the cricket bag, half run, half hobble to catch up.

'Will it be a Test match?'

'Only if Billy and the others are there.' If the rest were there, it wouldn't be too bad. Better than nothing anyway. We reached the point where part of the fence was so loose we could swing it to one side on a rusty old nail and make a gap to squeeze through then drag the bag after us. It didn't take long to see that neither Billy nor anyone else had bothered to turn up. Of course, they'd be at the fair like the others. They wouldn't be wasting their time on cricket. Only Tom was there, wearing his old umpire's coat, ploughing his mowing machine up and down the square ready for the season to start. Funny thing that. The start of the cricket season and the end of football. One day you just knew somehow and you would go to the cupboard under the stairs, push the football into the back corner and drag out the battered old leather bag where we kept the bats and stumps and things. It was also funny that Mrs Pike knew as well because that was when she started selling toffee apples, which Mother said was against the law because sugar rationing was still on and she must have got it on the black market though I don't see what the colour's got to do with it. I asked Father why we changed over and he said it always happens when you see the first swallow or hear a cuckoo or something. Not that I'd ever heard a cuckoo or even a swallow for that matter.

While I was waiting for Paul to catch up, I picked up a stone and threw it to scatter a flock of starlings. 'Not much point playing if no one else's here.'

'They might come later.' Paul started to open the bag and spoke into its depths, still not wanting to look me in the eye. 'Do you want to bat or bowl?' He offered me the ball as if it was a present or something. 'You can be England, if you want.'

'Right. One game. I only promised one game. That's one innings each.'

'It's two in a Test match.' Paul rolled the ball in my direction then turned to rummage about in the bag once more.

'Does this look like a Test match?' I half flung my arms in the air in disgust. 'Well, does it?' But deep down I knew I was being unfair. Even if there were only two of us, we always played Test matches. England v Australia, proper innings, eleven-a-side, batting and bowling, right- or left-handed like the real players did. Paul emerged from the bag holding our battered Rexine-covered scorebook. 'No time for scoring, just keep count. Two innings each, you've got one batsman, one bowler and that's it. Choose your players.' While he was making up his mind, I weighed up the odds. 'Come on, England's won the toss, you're batting.' I needed to think about this carefully, decide on the best way to do it. Put Australia in, bowl them out, bat myself, smash a few, declare, bowl them out again and I'd kept my promise and, if I got a move on, I might catch Mike and the others before they caught the bus. Even if I caught the next one, I might still find them before they disappeared into all the noise and the dark. Paul could take the stuff home and tell Mother what had happened. There'd still be trouble but at least I'd have had a ride on the new big dipper. But I'd have to get a move on. There was no time to hang about.

Paul had taken the stumps out of the bag and was trying to find the stump holes made during previous games. 'Further left, much further left, there, there they are, right under your nose.' I picked up the single remaining stump and lifting my arm above my shoulder speared it into the ground at the bowler's end.

'That's not twenty-two yards.'

I had no time to argue. 'It'll do.' As I measured out my run I noticed the starlings were beginning to sort themselves out and settle in a long row along the top of the sight screen. They looked quite funny sitting there, like the old men who sat in front of the pavilion when a proper match was on. Quite a lot of the members wore blazers with different-coloured stripes A bit like the starlings but more like parrots really. They certainly sounded like parrots. One of them would say, 'Well played, sir.' And then the others would all start saying it. I'm not sure why they always call the cricketers 'sir', it's not as though they are school teachers or anything. I scraped a mark at the end of my run, turned up the collar of my shirt like the 'Bomber' always does, and selected my grip on the ball with fingers on each side of the seam. 'PLAY!' Then, head down, I turned and began my run up, only to judder to a halt. At the far end of the pitch Paul was standing up straight, one hand held up, palm outwards.

'What's wrong now?'

'Middle and leg, please.'

'You don't need a guard.'

'Yes, I do. Father says if you don't do it properly, don't do it at all.' I glared at my younger brother and turned once more to measure out my run. If he wanted it properly, that's what he'd get... twenty-three, twenty-four, twenty-five. '*PLAY!*'

It was not easy to tell *how* it happened. Perhaps the evening air had made my fingers clammy and the ball had slipped. Perhaps it was because I was trying too hard. Perhaps because the pitch was a bit shorter than it should have been. But there was no doubting *what* happened. Instead of the ball bouncing on the pitch as it should do, it flew head height towards Paul. He started to step forward as if he was going to hit it, then in midstroke suddenly straightened and tried to put his hand in front of his face but the handle of his bat must have got caught up in his jumper. It was a terrible sound, like the sharp crack of a rifle. Paul made a noise which seemed to be somewhere between a cough and a cry before crumpling to the ground.

I took a few steps down the pitch. The starlings, as one, had risen in a great clatter and began to circle the ground. 'Are you all right?' Complete silence. Tom must have turned off his machine. Then I heard him calling to his assistant and start running towards us, the tails of his umpire's coat flapping behind him. The caretaker, startled by the tone of voice, stuck his head out of the door, disappeared, then returned, jacket half on, half off, to run after the groundsman. Then hearing Tom shout something, he turned round and legged it back towards the pavilion. I walked a further few paces down the pitch. 'Come on, Paul. You'll be all right.'

I didn't know where they had all come from, but suddenly, somehow, there seemed to be a crowd of people. Tom was now telling everyone what to do. 'Billy, you know where he lives. Tell his mam to come quick. Joe, get the keys for the big gates. You'll have to open both of them to let it get in. Come on, man, get a move on. Billy!' Billy's head reappeared through the hole in the fence. 'Tell her we've phoned for one. Quick as you can, lad!' Where had Billy come from? He should have been at the fair by now. Everyone seemed to be shouting at everyone else so I thought the best thing was to pull out the stumps and put them with the ball back in the bag. I saw someone had rolled up their coat and put it under Paul's head. The starlings, by now, had once more settled into their seats on the sight screen.

Mother and the ambulance made their entrance together. I could see each was trying to outmanoeuvre the other. 'Oh, there you are, what on earth's happened?' As usual Mother had decided to take charge of things just like she always does at the coffee mornings for the League of Pity. 'Yes, I can see it was an accident – no, thank you, young man, we can manage perfectly well ourselves.' I could see that Billy had hoped to help carry the stretcher but, startled by Mother's tone of voice, stopped and just picked up one of the ambulancemen's bags instead. Mother had now started to talk to Tom. 'Thank you, groundsman. I will let my husband know how promptly you acted. Oh, for goodness sake, stop that noise.' The ambulance siren obediently fell silent.

Somewhere in all this, Aunt Helen had arrived and took my hand. 'We'll have to go, now. We can't stay here.' She led me to a gate at the far end of the ground and after we got home said it was best if I went to my bedroom.

I heard the front door shut and someone starting to come upstairs. I could tell by the sound that it wasn't Mother or Aunt Helen so that means it must be Father. He's home from work much earlier than usual, so someone must have told him. I could hear his voice as he spoke to Mother. Different from normal, more like the voice he used when he took me to the court where he works when he's wearing his wig. *Well was it an accident or was it not?* I knew what the question would be but I wasn't sure what was the right answer. It'll be like that time when I got 100 per cent in the end-of-year arithmetic exam and the next year, just as I was about to leave the house, Mother said, *Make sure you get 100 per cent again.* Then after Mr Allen read out the results I told her I had got 100 per cent again when I'd only got 87 per cent. I don't know why I said that because I knew they would find out sooner or later. In fact it was sooner because Father had gone to see the headmaster to see if I was clever enough to go to the next school and I expect the headmaster said I wasn't because I had only got 87 per cent. And then there was an inquest. We always had an inquest when things didn't go right. I don't really know what an inquest is but that's what they call it and it usually ends with people raising their voices and sometimes Mother walks out of the room. I suppose there will be another inquest about Paul.

*Come on, this is a straightforward matter. A simple question demands a simple answer. 87 per cent is not 100 per cent, is it?* As if to prove the point, Father had taken out of his pocket the box of Swan Vestas that he uses to light his pipe and placed it so half of the box overhung the edge of the table. *You see this box of matches? It is either on the table, or –* with a sharp chop of his finger he sent it spinning to the floor – *it's off. In matters like this, my boy, the truth is the truth. There are no ifs, no buts.*

I got off the bed and walked over to the table under the window. It seemed a long time ago since I was hurrying but not rushing to get the last bit glued into place. It's a funny thing, time. When you're out playing you can leave the house after breakfast and it seems no time at all before someone is shouting you to come in for lunch but when you're put in detention after school the time seems to drag on for ages and ages. I picked up the fuselage of the model plane, holding it up to the light so that the shadows of the criss-cross construction fell on the polished wooden surface. Mike might have said it was strong but it didn't look strong to me. It would take not much more than one blow with my fist to smash the whole thing to smithereens.

## THE LAST WALTZ

It's not often you get a win-win-*win* situation and it certainly didn't look like that at the time.

*

You couldn't call it a corridor. It was far too wide for that, but it certainly wasn't what most people would term a room. At one time, no doubt, its purpose would have been obvious but centuries of construction, destruction and reconstruction had reduced it to little more than a ridiculously large cupboard. A space with two doors, one on the north side that led down a shallow set of steps into the Quad, the other on the east that led into that *sanctum sanctorum* – the Senior Prefects' Court. Here these eight good men and true would dispense justice employing (short of capital punishment) the usual tools of retribution and deterrent.

This corridor-cupboard was where the presumed-guilty waited for the court to assemble. As a waiting room it was singularly bereft – neither pictures of obscure artists nor out-of-date copies of *National Geographic* relieved the gloom.

Nothing but a clock with an audible tick. Though I'd never been there before, I instinctively knew what to do. You enter up the steps, close the door behind you, walk to the far end of the cul-de-sac, face the wall and wait. Wait until they decided to arrive. Wait with the ticking of the clock.

I suppose it must have been Neddie after all. A pity after I'd made such an effort with my Greek prose just to please him.

The whole farrago (my word of the week courtesy Soc & Pol) had started on what turned out to be Friday the 13th. The bell had rung to signify the end of Jaggers, and the Weasel with his pack of prefects filed into the common room for evening prayers. Mumbling over, there was a pause. Instead of the usual gown-flowing exit, the housemaster held his ground, cleared his throat and announced that Saturday morning school had been cancelled and, instead, in anticipation of the annual dance with the local girls' high school, the house would report to the refec for compulsory dance practice. Apparently last year the occasion of the dance had resembled more a rugby scrum than a demonstration of courtesy and poise. I say 'apparently' as this was the first year I was sufficiently senior to attend this much-heralded event.

Saturday morning duly arrived and Tossington-Smythe, Head of House, climbed on to a refectory chair and coughed several times. 'After last year's disgraceful behaviour, though I am relieved to say that the worst excesses were perpetrated by School House, I expect our behaviour to be impeccable. The house, at all times, will remain on or in the vicinity of the dance floor and under no circumstances stray into any other room or the school gardens. An apparent excuse offered for this anti-social behaviour was that some of you were not confident about the art of dancing and spent the night among the bushes to avoid embarrassment. This year all that will change. The House will learn to dance and Matron has kindly offered to instruct. Constable will be in charge of the gramophone and change the record as required. The maxim I want the House always to keep in mind is "Going to a dance means going there *to* dance." With that in mind I can foresee no problem. Over to you, Matron.'

All eyes turned in her direction. It was probably the abandonment of her white coat of office and choice of a rather low-cut dress that caused the atmosphere to change. There was, so to speak, a visible perking up all round.

'Right, boys, we will start with the waltz followed by the foxtrot and quickstep and if we have time, we can run through Strip the Willow.' (Perhaps, given the reaction in certain quarters, not the wisest of choices.) 'First, I want you to pair off according to year, Junior Study, Senior Study and the rest, then decide between you who is going to lead. Yes, lead as in male partner. Come on! Come on! It can't be that difficult. I'm sure you do something like this before every rugger warm-up.'

Amid a mixture of threats and promises, compromises were made and the House stood in rather sullen pairs. Inevitably there was an odd number. Matron clapped her hands briskly. 'Never mind, I will need a demonstration partner. Clare! You'll do.' No surprise there. Johnny Clare – everyone liked JC. All the girls fancied him and most of the lads fancied being him. Even the Weasel liked him and the Weasel liked nobody. To my mind he was a combination of James Dean and Simon Templar (my last and latest heroes).

Matron, ignoring an undercurrent of suppressed ribaldry, was now in full swing adopting her I-am-clapping-my-hands-so-pay-attention approach. 'The waltz is a dance in triple time which allows the dancers to elegantly rotate as they...' Typical. Here we go again '... basic steps. The gentleman steps forward...' Par for the course. They cancel morning school then fill the gap with more lessons '... forward with the right foot, steps left with his left foot then brings his right...' Even European History was better than this. 'And one... two, three. Do pay attention Smithson...' At least with European you could shift the monotonous drone on to his war experiences '... the gentleman places his hand firmly around the lady's waist. Not that firmly, Clare.'

'*Excuse me, sir. Catherine the Great, sir. Didn't she want to get a foothold in the Mediterranean, sir.*'

'*Ah yes the Med. Did I ever tell you boys about that time in Crete when...*'

'Come on Smithson. I'm sure he won't bite you. Constable! The record – please. Now, boys, and one, two, three...' One bloody two bloody three. The whole thing reminded me of rifle drill during Friday's combined cadet force. 'Up two three – cross two three – down two three!'... sans, of course, the obligatory swearing from some uppity NCO. And so it went on – reverse steps, spins, slow tempo, quick tempo... 'It's a ball you're going to, Smithson, a ball, not Saturday night at the local *palais de dance*'... foxsteps and quicktrots until eventually even Matron had had enough. In fact, I thought she looked a little ruffled by the end. JC, of course, danced effortlessly throughout.

'Well done, boys. Enjoy yourselves on Tuesday.'

Odd day to have a dance, Tuesday. There again, I suppose Friday's an odd day to practise killing people.

I had let the others get ahead before slipping through the squeeze stile that led to the river banks. There might well be safety in numbers, but I fancied a fag and if you are going to risk a beating you may as well cut down the odds. An orange glow concealed inside the cup of one hand has a better chance of avoiding detection than a battery of glowing cigarette ends. Anyway, it was a shortcut. Down past the boathouse, over the bridge and through the close was quicker than jostling your way through the narrow streets of Old Town.

But there was still one problem if you wished to avoid being caught. Some luminary, no doubt, had decided the school should be distinguished from the common herd by the wearing of a stiff-brimmed straw boater (aka basher). No matter how you wore it – on the back of the head, tilted to one side or even forward to resemble some brooding film star – you could not remove the air of appearing faintly ridiculous. But more to the point, they were very conspicuous. Once off the school premises they had to be worn and it was regarded as a serious matter if you didn't. They were not like a cap you can slip in and out of your pocket as and when required. You might as well try to conceal a soup tureen under your coat. Smoking while wearing a basher was a complete giveaway. Some earnest member of the public would be on to the head in a flash. On the other hand, not wearing a basher was irrefutable evidence you were up to no good. You were damned if you did and damned if you didn't. But, as Socrates might or might not have mentioned, necessity is the mother of invention, so I had managed to retrieve a long-abandoned item of straw headwear and by the judicious use of scissors and Sellotape had been able to produce a collapsible version. It took only a second or two to make it sufficiently flat so it could be hidden under a jacket and, should circumstances dictate, not that much longer to resurrect it into something that would pass for the genuine article. To give it a final touch, I had managed to acquire a hatband in the colours of a house other than my own. They set the rules. You try to break them.

I was halfway down the unlit track that led to the boathouse when suddenly a figure loomed out of the darkness. It stepped into my path then stopped as if trying to weigh me up. I was too busy trying to get rid of the cigarette to get a good look, but from what I had seen, it might well have been my Classics master. Was it Neddie or was it that weirdo who offered Smithson half a crown to show him his willy? Anyway, it doesn't matter that much. Even if it was Neddie, masters generally weren't a problem. They tried to avoid any confrontation and left it to the prefects to thrash the school into submission. And Neddie was a good bloke and, if I couldn't be sure it was him, he probably couldn't be sure it was me. If it had been the Weasel, it would have been a different matter. The Weasel was not only my housemaster but looked for any excuse to swing the right arm. Perhaps I'd better give up smoking. They say it's bad for your health.

The rest of the journey went without incident and, basher reassembled, it wasn't long before I caught up with a couple of friends. It was a funny feeling walking through the front door of a girls' school, a bit like entering a nunnery, I suppose. Mind you, I have to admit they'd made a bit of an effort. A pair of girls took your coat and pressed what they rather cleverly called a *terpsicordial* into your hand. As cocktails go, it looked the part with umbrellas and stuff together with a slice of something red floating on the surface. On closer examination it unfortunately smelt and tasted of orange and lemonade. The entertainment had spread to balloons and bunting, and the lights had been shaded with some sort of crepe paper to soften the normally institutional glare. Even the heating had been turned up from 'miser rate' giving the whole thing an air of what I supposed passed for sophistication. But what struck me most were the framed photographs, the pictures that adorned the length and breadth of the hall. Each and every one of them had been turned to face the wall (perhaps to stop the young gentlemen getting too excited at the sight of bare knees). Of course, after last year's debacle there was a strong if shadowy show of staff, mostly female as you would expect. Though I did catch sight of a male who looked like one of our geography teachers, but as he was wearing a suit, I couldn't be sure.

It was only when the music veered from what might have been an undercooked version of 'Greensleeves' into a cymbal-clashing, trumpet-blaring announcement of 'Alexander's Ragtime Band', that the full realisation of what was about to happen dawned on me. Seeing (or not seeing) Neddie had pushed the worst implications of the evening to the back of my mind. Now they flooded across the foremost part of my consciousness. To paraphrase The Tosser – the bad part of going to a dance is you'll probably be expected *to* dance. And to put it simply, I couldn't.

Anyone running the rule over the form book of my 'terpsicordial' activities would find it rather thin. There had been an occasion, at the age of seven, when I had been forced to attend a birthday party against my mother's, as it turned out, better judgement, and had won the spot prize. Or to be more precise, Billy Thompson and myself had shared that honour by ignoring conventional partnerships and completing the course by crossing hands and rotating at high speed. This conflation of whirling dervish and combine harvester inevitably scattered the rest of the contestants to the extremities of the dance floor where they cowered clutching their teddy bears. So, when the music stopped we were, so to speak, the last men standing. I seem to remember my mother took me home soon after that.

Any further experience was limited to dances arranged ostensibly for the benefit of the local League of Pity but actually for mothers to compare offspring and hats. However, the dances on offer were just stuff like the Gay Gordons and Strip the Willow – not so much dancing as skipping around to Jimmy Shand and his Band. At the time, I found girls not only boring but inclined to be bossy. The modus operandi, as I recall, was to avoid them as much as possible and get at the cream cakes and chocolate éclairs before they did. Not so much a social occasion as gang warfare.

Even Matron's dancing instruction had not been of much help. Like the combined cadet corps and cross-country running, her 'one, two, three' had felt like another of the pointless things you were forced to do to fill in the time between breakfast and lights out. I could manage the numbers game in theory and was even the not particularly proud possessor of *Our First Steps in the Ballroom* (a sixteenth-birthday present from a well-meaning aunt), the pages of which were covered with footprints moving in a bewildering fashion. But I had quickly discovered that knowing the steps doesn't mean you can dance, any more than knowing the vocab of a foreign language means you can parley with the natives.

I had just decided that my best plan was to spend the bulk of the evening in the Gents cloakroom when it happened. If there was a blast on a whistle, I didn't hear it, but the result was very similar to an assault from the trenches in the First World War. Platoons of young ladies swarmed across no man's land and seized the first boy they could lay hands on. Apparently, the opposition had also been informed that a dance meant dancing and they were not to stand on the niceties of convention.

My partner was older, taller and, judging from the way she clamped her right hand on my left shoulder, considerably stronger than me. After a step or two she arched her back so she could get a better look at my face.

'Don't I know you?'

She was one of those girls who hung over the wall of the school grounds so they could converse with any passing sixth-form boys that took their fancy. JC and his cronies were regular attendees and on one occasion they had decided to take me along. I'm not sure why. I suppose I was a bit like a pet monkey, though I didn't think so at the time.

'No, I don't think so.'

The next half hour or so was a succession of quick twirls, thank yous, then flight, during the course of which I discovered from a small red-haired girl they had been instructed to dance with any boy they found seated. Once their mission of mercy had been thrice completed they were free to dance with whomever they liked. It was a relief to sit and listen to the band. Interspersed with the usual drone of the 'Top Twenty' were one or two good bits where the saxophonist sounded a bit like Charlie Parker, and the cessation of enforced conviviality gave me the opportunity to watch the master at work. JC seemed to attract girls without any obvious effort. Those he talked to stood attentively, heads tilted to one side. Others would give an affectionate squeeze of the arm as they went past, while a random collection would hover in the middle ground. Somehow, he seemed to have time for them all and they for him. Eventually, I worked it out. It was something to do with smiling. He knew when to smile when it mattered.

I was just thinking it hadn't been too bad after all when the music stopped and, amid a clash of timpani, the band leader announced 'The Last Waltz'. I couldn't duck this one. Being the only person sitting out was not an option. I considered and discarded the lavatorial escape route. Too cowardly – even for me. Whichever way you looked at it, the time had come to ask a girl to dance. The options were fast running out when I noticed a girl who had half smiled at me when we passed in the passageway. Fearing the worst, I ploughed my way through the couples already on the floor. 'Would you like the last?'

At least she hadn't said no. It was difficult to know what she was thinking. Should I say something? Better not, just concentrate on the dancing if you can call it that. One... two, three. One, two...

'Why do you stop?'

Immediate panic. What did she say – was it why *don't* you stop? Stop what? Stop dancing?

'Sorry. I didn't quite catch that.'

'I said why do you stop?'

Yes, it was definitely do, not don't.

'Sorry. Stop what? '

'Stop at each corner. You dance really well down the side of the hall but when we reach a corner you stop, turn a right angle, then carry on.'

'I'm sorry, the book didn't deal with corners.'

Eventually, 'Sleepy Lagoon' came to its soulful end and I expected her to flee like the rest. Instead she just stood there for a moment as if waiting for me to say something. Eventually, I came out with the best I could manage.

'Do you live near the school?'

'No, Bankburn. I'll have to catch a bus.'

'Could I see you to the bus station, then?'

'Well. Yes. That would be nice.'

'Right. I'll just get my coat. See you at the front door.'

I managed to wriggle my way to the front of the queue.

'Yes, that's mine. The one next to the radiator. No, no the other one, the one with a hood.'

Twisting around, I put on my coat, then jamming the collapsed straw remnants out of sight, elbowed my way back to the front door. At first, I thought she had gone, then suddenly her face was framed by a gap in the crowd. She gave a wave, not a great arm-swinging signal but with a hand raised to her face with fingers that opened and closed.

We had just turned into Bishopsgate when she suddenly stopped with a look of alarm. 'Where's your straw hat? Did you forget it?'

'No and, anyway, it's called a basher. Only girls wear straw hats.'

'I call it a straw hat. Aren't you supposed to be wearing it?'

'Yes.'

'Then why aren't you? Where is it anyway?'

'It makes me look stupid and it's also a bit broken.'

She frowned, as if half expecting a joke. 'What do you mean – broken?'

'Well, not so much broken as rearranged.' I opened the top of my duffel coat and pulling out the bits began to re-assemble what might well have passed muster in the dark but under the glare of the street light looked pathetic. She looked at the remnants and began to smile. 'More battered than basher, I'd say. Come on then, put it on.'

'There. I told you I'd look stupid.'

'No more than the rest. Come here.' She put her left hand on my shoulder and with her right tilted the brim at an angle. 'There you are. That makes you look like whosit, you know, Humphrey Bogart, in *African Queen*.'

I wasn't at all sure how to respond to that. For all I knew she might be having a laugh at my expense. JC would have known. He would have made some sort of remark that girls laugh at. But I would only mess it up. Best go on the defensive.

'He didn't wear that sort of a hat. In fact, I don't think he wore a hat at all.'

'Of course he did. You must remember *that*. I don't believe you've even seen the film.'

Well, as that was true, it was more or less a conversation-stopper and we walked on in silence. Smooth your way out of that, JC.

The bus station was far busier than I had imagined it would be at that time of night.

'Well, that's my bus.'

'That one?'

'Yes. Number 27.'

A lengthy pause. There must be something I could say.

'Well, I suppose I'd better get on.'

'Yes, I'll just wait until it goes.'

'Oh, you needn't do that.'

'No problem really.'

'Well, I'd better get on then. Thank you for a very nice evening.'

'Apart from the dancing.'

'Don't worry. The dancing was fine. I really must go.'

'Of course you must. I hope I'll see you again. Could you give...'

She had already stepped on to the platform before I had finished the sentence. She turned as if to reply but a sudden surge of passengers, fearing the bus would go without them, bustled her down the aisle towards a seat at the front. Almost simultaneously the bus coughed into life.

I wandered back to the house with a sort of mixed feeling I couldn't quite work out. Maybe it was the route I had taken, for suddenly the streets seemed deserted. It's odd walking through a town at night. You feel as though you're in a box with a lid you can feel but not see. Last time I did something like this was with Billy Wright when for some stupid reason we decided to go for an early morning run and nicked a bottle of milk from a doorstep.

It wasn't that long before I reached the house and made my way to the junior/senior dorm. Eventually the usual banter stuttered to an end and I lay on my back staring at the ceiling. Yes, all was... what was that word Rev. Greg keeps on using... behovely? Yes, that was it. All was behovely. At least, it was until morning assembly when the Head of House announced I was to attend Senior Prefects' Court immediately after lunch.

The clock struck one. Now it will begin. I had seen it all before. First, they gathered outside the chapel. Then in single file cross the green, past the fives courts, through the eye of the needle of the great oak doors that led into the quad. I was still trying to imagine what stage this procession might have reached when the north door slammed inwards. The usual rigmarole – canes in right hands, boards on, slightly tilted, tassels to the left one inch off-centre. Ritual tap on the door jamb. One by one, they entered the court, the Head of School followed by his deputy, then heads of house, in strict order of foundation, followed by their deputies, the last slamming the door behind him. Behind the closed door the preliminaries began. First a shuffling of furniture, then after a short pause a series of thuds followed by a muffled crash. More shuffling, this time of feet, then silence. I risked a look at the clock. Seven minutes past one. I'd be late for afternoon games.

'Come!'

I opened the door and walked into the room.

'Door!'

I turned, closed the door, took a few paces forward then stopped. The room had been arranged so the heads of house and their deputies formed an avenue leading to an upturned chair. Beside the chair, as if left there by accident, was an oddly striped cushion. The Head of School, Thompson, stood at the head of the avenue. He was clearly going to initiate the inquisition.

'You are aware that breaking bounds is forbidden.'

I mistakenly thought Thompson's remark was a statement, so said nothing.

'Dumb insolence will get you nowhere. Are you aware that breaking bounds is forbidden?'

'Yes, Thompson.'

'After the dance on Tuesday night you were seen returning to school along Bishopsgate. Is that right?'

I was now utterly confused. I had assumed it was smoking. That it was Neddie who had seen me and informed the authorities after all. After the dance? But Neddie saw me on the way to the dance. Not after. What on earth was going on?

'Come on! Answer the question.'

'I was just seeing...'

'I am not interested in what you were seeing, just or otherwise. Were you in Bishopsgate on Tuesday night?'

'Yes, Thompson.'

'So, you were breaking bounds.'

'I didn't realise there was a set route. I just assumed you could...'

'The return route was clearly delineated in Monday morning notices.'

So that was it. Monday morning was Eng Lit followed by Greek, and the Hellenic scholars were sufficiently few to be stuffed into a cubbyhole in what used to be the belfry at the top of the tower. No doubt the little erk whose job it was to tour the classrooms with the morning notices had either been unaware of the belfry's existence or too idle to climb the three flights of spiralling stairs.

Thompson was clearly getting agitated by my silence and tried again. 'Do you agree you were seen breaking bounds?'

'Yes, I suppose so.'

'There is no suppose about it. Either you were or you weren't. I'll ask you again. Were you breaking bounds?'

'Yes, Thompson.'

'And you are aware that that is a beatable offence?'

'Yes, Thompson.'

'Very well. It's the decision of the court you'll be beaten three. Do you wish to appeal?'

No one ever appealed. To appeal to the headmaster was the ultimate disgrace, like abandoning your arms in the face of the enemy.

'No, Thompson.'

So, it wasn't Neddie to blame after all. It was all my bloody parents' fault. Over the years one or the other had dished out advice on personal behaviour, both public and private, much of which centred around the relative merits of triumph and disaster and taking advantage of fleeting opportunity. But among these many precepts that had strewn the stages of my childhood, there was one that had stood out as seeming more relevant than the rest. *Never, never allow a young lady to walk home alone in the dark.* But that's the trouble with parental values. They don't always work out for the best.

At this point in the proceedings, the Head of School had been pronouncing on the long-term benefits of accepting discipline before nodding to one of his fellows and joining one side of the avenue.

Shit! Up to then, I had not been too worried. Beatings by school prefects were usually fairly benign. By the time they reached such a lofty office, the novelty had worn off and they regarded it more as a duty than a pleasure. But there's always an exception. The designated administrator of punishment had risen rapidly through the ranks and had yet to establish his reputation. Not only was Wardle Captain of Fives but rowed bow in the 1st IV. Shit! This was going to hurt. Shit! Shit! Shit!

'Pick it up.' Wardle indicated the upturned chair. I walked up to the chair and stood it upright. Doing so, I had to push the cushion to one side. What I had taken for a rather bizarre pattern was in fact a series of parallel chalk marks.

'Bend over the chair.'

I leant over the chair and grasped the sides.

'Not there. Hold the front rail.'

Unlike a bullet, you heard this missile coming. A faint woosh through the air before the explosion. Three steps back. One – two – woosh. After the third there was a pause, but I knew enough to remain motionless. Any assumption on my part would mean another three. 'Right. You may leave.' I stood upright and walked to the door trying to appear indifferent to the pain.

'Wait! Haven't you forgotten something?'

I half turned. 'Thank you, Wardle.'

By the time I reached the changing rooms, they were deserted. The order of the day was 'CH:EX'. In theory, 'changed exercise' meant you could do any sport the school offered. In practice, it meant cross-country running. The standard and obligatory course was known as Broughton's – no doubt after the sadist that devised it. Apart from two short sections of road, it lay across clay-heavy fields interspersed with a couple of clarty root-tripping sections of woodland. There was, however, a variant known as Little Broughton's which missed out most of the fields and all the wooded section by taking a shortcut along a well-made farm track. Taking this shortcut was strictly forbidden. Ah well, looks like sheep and lamb time again.

The subsequent and compulsory cold shower drew the inevitable cacophonous inquest.

*Three on the same spot* (obviously, the chalked rehearsal had paid dividends).

*Christ, that must have hurt.*

*Yellow already. He must have really laid into you.*

*It's not just a matter of strength.*

*It's all in the wrist, you know. The way you cock it.*

*Pretty good shot anyway.*

The odd thing was, after it was all over, something appeared to have changed. People seemed to be weighing me up as if seeing me for the first time. Boys I had never spoken to started to greet me like a long-lost friend. For some time, I was confused. It couldn't have been the beating. It was bad but not that bad. It wasn't as if I'd done a Dai Thomas who, as legend had it, after a particularly vigorous beating had stood up and enquired of his assailant if that was the best he could manage. No, it was really nothing much more than the standard three. It was only later that week when JC passed me in the corridor and gave me a wink with 'Plenty of shop doorways on Bishopsgate, eh?' that the penny dropped. Apparently, a combination of rumour and gossip had cast me as some latter-day Casanova.

It was the following Sunday I crossed the river and made my way along its banks. For some unspecified reason you're allowed to go anywhere you want on Sunday but as often as not I would gravitate towards the cathedral. Not out of any religious conviction, you understand. On the contrary, after my mother had explained to me the implication of the word 'vocation' as an irresistible force that cannot be denied, I harboured a morbid fear of being compelled to become a vicar. No, I went to the cathedral because I liked the place. It had a sense of seriousness that I took to, especially if things weren't going all that well. In such circumstances, I'd cross the green towards the great south door, casting myself as the panting fugitive escaping from the hue and cry that followed, my eyes focused, intent only on clutching the hagoday, begging admittance from the hooded monks who, crouched by the door, stood ready for such an emergency. Everyone else calls the beast's head with a ring clasped between its grinning teeth a sanctuary knocker, but I discovered 'hagoday' was the proper word. I think it's quite cool to have a word no one else knows.

But on this occasion, I had a different reason for going there, so I crossed the river by New Bridge to gain entrance through the crypt at the west end of the building. As I approached, I was surprised to see a school four on the river. They don't usually row on a Sunday. There must be some big regatta or something. The coach (Oxford man, 4th in Geography) bellowed instructions through his loudhailer while trying to prevent his bike from wobbling into the reed beds. *Long! Keep it long, three. Wrists, boys, wrists. Cock the wrists!*

Bike and boat disappeared round a bend leaving only the cox's squeaky voice floating in the wind. A family of ducks re-emerged from the reeds to move downstream in an effortless flotilla. I quite liked that. I am not sure why but it seemed to sum everything up.

It was the time of day I particularly liked. The cheeriness of matins had melted and the solemnity of evensong had yet to descend. There was always a quiet as if the building was waiting for something to happen, someone to appear. But this Sunday, I knew what I was doing, for this was the Sunday in the month when the tower was open to visitors. I had waited all week to find somewhere where I would be alone. I paid sixpence and ascended the 218 feet that separated bottom from top. Once up, I paused to look over the surrounding countryside. But I wasn't here for the view. I wanted to read the letter properly without someone peering over my shoulder. I pulled it out of my jacket pocket taking care the wind didn't catch it and carefully opened it up in the shelter of one of the parapets.

*I am writing to thank you for seeing me to the bus on Tuesday and to tell you I really enjoyed the evening. The whole atmosphere was wonderful wasn't it? But the real reason is to let you know how bad I felt when I heard you'd been punished because of me and I can't tell you how sorry I am that the whole thing was my fault. But there's a bit of a good side. It's turned out that you are a bit of a hero with the girls in my class. I expect they will start hanging over the wall hoping to see you. I expect you'll be going home for Christmas very soon, but I hope we can meet again next term. I'm not sure. Our teachers are quite strict about that sort of thing. Anyway, I hope you're all right now and it didn't hurt too much.*

*Best Wishes and a Very Happy 1957.*
*Jennifer*

*

The win-win-win situation? It wasn't until later I got the affair in some sort of perspective. It is probably stretching it a bit to say I got the girl and the glory but I had started to learn there's a bit more to life than being Johnny Clare or even James Dean for that matter.

## THE GRAMMAR SCHOOL MASTER

When I think back, I am not really sure why or even how I first got into teaching. I can remember one stage of my life when there were various lengthy and pointless discussions, or rather suggestions, that ran the gamut of the so-called professions. But from actuary to zoologist, all drew a blank. If pressed I might admit to some vague idea of wanting to write, an ambition that was given a semblance of support by reading English at university and a variety of books written in the twentieth century, but when it came to filling the unforgiving minute, concrete evidence was pretty thin on the ground. Eventually there emerged the not unreasonable parental hint that they had supported me long enough, so I was left with no alternative but attempt to forge my own furrow or some such mixed metaphor and look for a job. At the last resort and in common with many other possessors of qualifications-of-no-practical-use, I applied for a post at one of the many establishments that specialise in preparing its pupils for the rigours of the greater (and lesser) public schools of England.

It turned out that, although the position advertised was for a Teacher of English to Common Entrance and Scholarship standard, the real burden of the post lay in the instruction of Latin to a number of small boys who had reached varying stages in their intellectual and social development. Nevertheless, though seven-year-olds lisping their way through the first conjugation to the tune of 'Life on the Ocean Waves' was not the height of intellectual stimulation, the job offered an unexpected plus side. By chance, I had found myself in a university town with a lively social scene. This, with vacations designed to save the school as much money as possible, made my occupational choice less of a chore, more a second and better-informed shot at student life. There was also the inestimable advantage of the return match being fully funded. To add to my good fortune the teacher of English (proper) decided at the end of the Michaelmas term to abscond with both the school games fund and the matron. So I found myself peremptorily promoted to fill his shoes.

It was not long before I decided that if I was going to do the job properly, I'd better get some sort of qualification, and after a year immersing myself in the likes of *Education: Its Data and First Principles* acquired the necessary ticket from the appropriate authority. Suitably armed, I applied to a number of grammar schools bearing illustrious names and to my surprise almost immediately found one that was mutually acceptable. Both parties having agreed terms, I left the interview and stood at the main gates trying to assess what I had let myself in for. At that moment the bell for end of school rang. Instead of the well-trained preparatory dribble of my previous experience there burst forth a torrent of vitality bordering on violence. O Brave New World indeed.

In due course I was handed my timetable that informed me I was not only to teach the thirty boys of form 3B but was also to be their form master. In common with the other trades that dress themselves up as professions, education has its 'mysteries'. The '3' signified not the third year but the first. Nor did 'B', as would be commonly supposed, mean the second cohort in the ranks of academic ability. Forms 1 and 2 were occupied by the nine- and ten-year-old pupils of the fee-paying junior school who on reaching eleven would, no doubt to keep their parents happy, automatically transfer to 3A. This favoured treatment meant 3B, C, D, etc. comprised the boys from the local primaries, placed in an order that reflected their notoriously unreliable eleven-plus results. The upshot of all this was the very brightest of pupils in any given year were as likely or even more likely to reside in what would appear to the outsider as the nether reaches of the groves of academe.

Although I might have started off with starry-eyed notions that the grammar school system would lead to social equality and a fairer society, it didn't take me long to see the whole thing was a sham. In an ever more complicated world the members of the Establishment, though not necessarily adept at the higher flights of human thought, at least had the nous to devise a system which would allow others to do the thinking for them. When they ran out of bright chaps of their own class, they had little alternative but to trawl the lower orders. Once the system was up and running, they could applaud their own initiative and return to the uninterrupted pleasure of pursuing smallish furry animals and odd-shaped balls. There was a bit of a problem of what to do with those that didn't make the cut, but no doubt those clever fellows we've selected will be able to sort something out.

For some reason, I thought I could redress the balance and missed no opportunity to express an opinion that in retrospect seems to have contained more rhetoric than substance. A not uncommon tirade was directed against those well-meaning folk who collect for charity. Charity, I would explain, was filling in for the government. It was the government's job – no, the government's duty – to provide for the needy, the ill, the bereft. What would happen when the do-gooders decided they had done their bit and called it a day? Who would pick up the pieces? While they were at it, why not go the whole hog and sell raffle tickets to increase our stockpile of nuclear weapons? And the staff room was no better. No doubt well-meaning, senior members would take me to one side and suggest that I should change my views if I 'wanted to get on'. But that was the trouble – I didn't want to get on, or off, or in any other direction for that matter. I thought I was right and that was the end of it.

I also had a strategic weapon in my struggle against what I saw as capitalist exploitation. Through the teaching of English, both Language and Literature, I hoped to open up minds not yet blunted by the cudgel of mortgage repayments. The very nature of the subject meant it encouraged individuality of thought and expression. At the beginning of their first term I would stand before the class and hold a new exercise book aloft. I would then suggest that this is not what it appeared to be. It was not the commonplace staple of paper covered in red cardboard that you will receive in other lessons. This is different because within this book I will find you, because only you will write in this book and you will write what you think, what you believe, what you know. It is your world and, when I enter your world, it will be a privilege, not a right. As a visitor, I will consider and try to appreciate your point of view and your opinions. If I offer mine, it is with respect and intending to help, as a guest might suggest a different way to unblock a sink or rid your garden of some pest that is destroying the roses.

I would then hand out a book individually to each pupil – not throwing them across the room as is often the practice – explaining that each book is unique as its purpose is not to contain answers to be marked right with a tick or wrong with a bad-tempered cross. Here is an empty space with no preconditions waiting for you to do whatever you decide.

And I soon learnt that as a teacher it was never enough to preach or cajole. You have first to catch the attention and, once caught, to hold it. The classroom was your theatre and you as the principal actor had to do better than strut and fret your hour upon the stage. You had to entertain, not playing the fool, but as a conjuror, pulling rabbits and silk handkerchiefs from the most unexpected of hats. The aim was for each lesson to be a show, a firework display that held the eye and concentrated the mind, yet, simultaneously, informed, directed and warned against unforeseen pitfalls.

One particular stunt never failed to impress. It would occur when, for the first time, I was explaining the importance of contrast to create tension. I would position myself at the side of an unoccupied desk. To start off with I would sit on it, shifting their point of focus from its accustomed position. Then as I was talking, I would stand up, open the desk lid and place my hand on its top edge as if seeking support. While doing this, I was explaining that if you wrote a story where dramatic action followed dramatic action without pause or contrast, the tension would slowly but surely ooze away. You must allow your story to breathe. It cannot hold its breath forever. It must ebb before it can flow. You must have silence before you have... At this point I would slam the lid down with all the force that one hand allowed. To give time for the effect to sink in, I would walk slowly back to my desk before turning and facing the class. Faces, half amused by the circus, half appalled by the violence, would look back.

There was also a ritual that developed over time. Every Sunday morning I would set off for school, let myself into the staff room, make a cup of coffee then walk the few yards down the main corridor to my and 3B's classroom. I always set Sunday morning aside to mark their weekly essay. I tried to explain that an essay was not a vehicle for punishment as in 'Write a thousand words on why it is wrong to throw snowballs at passing cars' but derived from the French verb *essayer*, to try or attempt. What they were engaged upon was an attempt to put down their feelings and views in such a way that the reader could understand what was in their mind. The first attempt might not entirely succeed but it would lay a cornerstone for future attempts and eventually, if they were patient, they would be able to say exactly what they meant. Also, at the end of their work they might find a comment, some thought of my own, but they would find no number, no $13\frac{3}{4}$ out of 20, no attempt by me to place a relative value on their work.

This method of marking did not meet with official approval but as I pointed out to the Senior Master, a mathematician, who had been sent to upbraid me on the heresy, there was a coincidence between the words 'mark' and 'mar' that perhaps was worth considering. And in the interest of standardisation could there be a ruling on whether the cos theta of *Hamlet* was greater or lesser that the square root of *Macbeth*. The point, however, seemed to have been lost on him. The row rumbled on for the rest of the term but eventually a truce was called and it was decided that if I could produce a form order which would both satisfy the parents and provide sufficient information for the yearly promotion and relegation of pupils, I could mark in my own fashion.

And within the overall ritual, I had developed a particular rite. I would divide the books into three separate piles, two large, one small. The latter contained the work of the most promising boys and I would save them for the last. Then I would walk down the aisles between the rows of desks, opening the lid of each one in turn so they stood before me like so many dominoes ready to be played, or tram seats waiting to be rearranged for the return journey. After each essay had been read and my comment added, I would place the book in the owner's desk and close the lid.

One down, twenty-nine to go. After the first baker's dozen, I would stop for a cigarette, after the second I would return to the staff room for a second cup of coffee. That left the remaining four. This select group deserved the greatest attention as they were more likely than not to contain something that would be helpful to Monday's discussion – or as 3B would have it, with 'the inquest'. Even these were arranged in a pecking order and on this occasion I had decided to leave David Smith's to last. He wasn't the most fluent of writers but he nearly always had something interesting and thoughtful to say

The title of the work set was 'A Moment of Real Disappointment'. I had taken some time to explain that before they put pen to paper, they should take time to think about the title. To look carefully at the words and decide what they really meant. To think whether the important word might well be 'moment' rather than 'disappointment'. This is what they were being asked to describe. A particular moment, the second or so when the disappointment, whatever it was, sank in. Of course, they would have to describe the events that led up to that moment but all the description should draw the reader towards the eventual outcome. When the moment arrived, the reader must be affected in some way, the tension that had been building up must be released. I didn't expect all the class of eleven-year-olds fully to understand what I was on about but if I got them into the habit of thinking what words really mean, then as they grew older and started to put things together they would, with a bit of luck, develop an independence of thought that would stand them in good stead for the rest of their lives. While we were about it, we should look at the word 'Real' and ask ourselves why it had been added to the title. What it didn't mean was 'very' or 'super' as in 'that was a real good book'. What I wanted was for them to write something based on their own experience. Something that was real to them. So, no spaceships and pirates, please!

I picked up the last book. A single raised desk lid flagged the end was nigh. That afternoon's work had taken longer than usual and I thought about switching on the light.

### *A Moment of Real Disappointment*
### *By David Smith*

*I remember I was a bit worried that morning on my way to my Primary School, called St John's which is on Mill Road. My Dad, though he had come home from hospital, had been told he must still stay in bed. If he didn't get better soon, he wouldn't be able to take me to see United on Saturday. This would be really disappointing. Although I enjoyed reading and numbers quite a lot and was on the top table at School what I really enjoyed was playing football in the afternoon after school.*

My Mum had made some really nice sandwiches which I ate while waiting for the boys from Prexton Prep to arrive. When they did they were quite snobby and you could see they thought we were ignorant and couldn't speak properly. But we didn't mind that as long as we won. My Dad says just because you speak posh it doesn't mean you can play football. I said that because you speak posh doesn't mean you can't play football either. Then my big sister Deborah told me not to be too big for your boots. I was going to say being too big for your boots wasn't much use at football but Mum gave me one of her looks so I didn't.

Anyway the boys from Prexton Prep arrived and they all had same colour shorts and socks as well as shirts. They wore bright red and looked very smart and quite big as well. The match kicked off and our teacher, Mr Weston, was the referee. It was soon clear that the Prexton Prep boys were very good at football and there would be a good hard match.

In the end it was a bit like that comic that Pete Barker lent me. The ball went from end to end. Each side in turn had the chance to score the vital goal. Then the moment happened. I had never scored before and if I am honest I have to admit that I was lucky to be in the team because Mrs Beswick says there was a shortage of boys in our year. So whatever Sarah Hopkins says we were always up against it.

Then it happened. Pete who was our best player kicked the ball towards their goalie. I thought it was going in. Their goalie made a good stop but it bounced from his hands and landed just in front of me. The goal was there, empty. I couldn't miss. I kicked the ball. Oh no! I thought I had missed but it hit the right side of the post and slowly tricked over the line. Prexton Prep kicked off again but almost at once Mr Weston blew his whistle. We'd won. All my team slapped me on the back. Even those who said I was a swot and sucked up to the teachers. The Prexton Prep boys just trooped off the field. Their teacher looked very angry.

*I couldn't wait to get changed and get home to tell Dad. I'd tell Mum, of course, but she wouldn't understand and just say "That's very nice, David". But Dad would understand. He used to tell me about the time when he played football himself and when he got better we would go to the Park and he would play in goal while I had shots in. He told me if I practised a lot I would get better and I had to listen what Mr Weston told me.*

*When I got home I threw my kit on the floor ready to ignore our Debbie's sarky remarks and started to run upstairs. Mum was standing at the top of the stairs looking funny. It's OK Mum, I'll put my bag away after. I just want to see Dad. I scored the winning goal. I whispered the last bit so he shouldn't hear yet.*

*I could see now that Mum was not angry. I stopped on the stairs. She walked down as far as me and sat down on the step and sat me on her knee. I'm afraid I've got some terrible news, David. I'm afraid Daddy is dead. He died this afternoon.*

*So I couldn't tell him about the winning goal and that was my moment of real disappointment.*

I put down my, by now, superfluous pen, picked up the book and walked over towards David's desk. Suddenly, I felt quite tired. I placed his book on top of all his other neatly piled books and in the now fast-fading light closed the desk lid without any perceptible sound.

## *THE DO-IT-YOURSELF MOVEMENT*

If there's one thing that really annoys me it's the invention of Alexander bloody Bell, that incessant ring that assumes you're at its beck and call. It's always for her, anyway. So why for God's sake doesn't she answer it. Ah yes, she said something about popping around to Marjory's. Of course, I could just let it ring until whoever it is gets tired of it. But, then, they'd only ring later and there again it is not impossible it might be important. I pushed the half-finished crossword to one side and went into the hall. 'Shothurst 765 942. Can I help you?'

'Ah yes. Good. Hello, sir. I don't know if you remember me – Dyson. You taught me English at the sec mod.'

'Sure, I remember you, Tyson. Upper Five Gardening, wasn't it? *Great Expectations* and all that.'

'No, sir, not Tyson. He was the year below me. This is Dyson, Sid Dyson. I was wondering, if it was not too inconvenient, if I could come and see you sometime?'

'Of course, Sid, any time. What's it all about?'

'I'd rather not discuss it over the phone. I'd like to talk about it in person, if I could. Would two o'clock this afternoon be OK?'

'Two o'clock would be fine.'

Sid Dyson. For the past year or two the name had started to slip from my memory but before that was a different story. It all started somewhere around my thirty-fifth birthday when I had decided, having reached the hinge of life, so to speak, that it was time to sort myself out. My first act, as an outward sign of an inner resolve, would be to chuck out all the stuff that had accumulated in the loft. So, I got out the stepladders from the cupboard under the stairs, placed them precisely under the trapdoor and climbed through the narrow aperture into the upper reaches of my estate. And that's how, during the subsequent fumblings in the half-light of a fast-fading torch, I found it. 'It' being a wallet file or more particularly Sid Dyson's wallet file, lying among the midden of unwanted wedding presents and pieces of carpet that might come in useful.

But there's little point in starting a story three quarters of the way through. So I'll try to go back to the beginning. Yet even if I returned to what was the start of what I now regard as the Dyson affair, to properly explain it I would have to travel even further back still. Now that I come to think of it, the whole saga is really a Russian doll of a tale. But as I must start somewhere, I'll start at the age of six. It was around then I decided I wanted to write a book and I accomplished this ambition by copying, word by word, one of Enid Blyton's *Five-Minute Tales* into a notebook I'd been given at Christmas. Over the years, my literary ambition flickered and wavered but the light never completely went out. Eventually I realised that if anything concrete was to come of it, I would have to give up the day job (the fiscal equivalent of the 'pram in the hall') and give the matter a proper shot. So, to précis, I wrote some stories which were mostly short and sent them to my literary agent called Long who thought short stories didn't sell unless you were already established and why didn't I try some of this post-modernist stuff which seems to be going down quite well at the moment. At which point the pram duly appeared in the shape of 7lb 12oz called Miranda. And along with the pram came the comments of it's all very well being a man of letters but the letters we are getting nowadays tend to be written in red.

So, I turned to the classifieds and there among the butchers and bakers and, no doubt, if you knew where to look, the odd candlestick maker, I came across an advert which had been placed by the local secondary modern school:

*Owing to sudden illness, urgently required until the end of the school year, English Teacher (graduate preferred) to teach up to and including O level. An interest in horticulture desirable but not essential.*

Application made. Interview fixed. Unsurprisingly, as the 'sudden illness' had befallen my predecessor in the middle of the Christmas term, there was limited competition for the job. A woman who confided that she would much prefer to teach little ones and an Australian backpacker who had already decided that he would rather work in a bar, came, saw and went. So, in due course, I dusted off my board rubber and presented myself at the secretary's office of Shothurst Secondary Modern School for Boys.

Time passed. Monthly pay cheques appeared, to the relief of all concerned. For my part I watched those under my care arrange the alphabet in a number of interesting ways and attempted to navigate my way through the variants of meaning of what, up to that point, I'd assumed were common and easily understood words. 'While' and 'must' were two particular examples. The latter caused particular confusion. The question *Must* I do this or that was not, as I had initially supposed, an expression of surly compliance, but simply a polite enquiry as to whether it was convenient for this or that to be done. But after a few weeks a working relationship was established where Lower Five Gardening were allowed to doze through my Friday afternoon reading of *Great Expectations* (with appropriate accents) in return for a regular supply of fresh fruit and vegetables. All was... for the most part... behovely. Then out of the blue a note appeared in my pigeonhole from the headmaster's secretary to the effect that I should present myself at her master's study as a matter of some urgency.

'Come in. Come in. Have a seat.' The head, George Augustus Barnfather, was a small round man whose only distinction was a glass eye. He liked to encourage the myth that he had lost the original fighting Rommel in the desert but the less glamorous truth was he had poked it out with a garden rake. 'How are you finding things? A bit different from the grammar, I'll be bound. No strolling through the glades of academe at Shothurst Secondary, eh?' I wasn't certain where this was going but suspected that Little Pip and tomatoes might have something to do with it, so muttered some platitude about each deserving according to his abilities and needs, and waited for developments.

'Abilities and needs. Exactly, that's why I wanted this little chat.' He leant forward, elbows on his desk, steepling his fingers in a manner he, no doubt, considered head-magisterial. 'I am sure you are aware that some – by no means all, of course – but some of the boys you teach might be described as late developers. As a matter of fact, I was just such a late developer myself. But that's of no consequence. What I was saying is those boys in this school who have had the misfortune to develop...' The tips of his fingers opened and closed as if searching for a precise definition. I decided to move the conversation on a step.

'Late?'

'Yes. Quite. Late. These boys, had they not been late, might have passed the eleven-plus and gone to the grammar.'

I had even less idea where this conversation was supposed to be going but I assumed, as the fingers had now been entwined and placed on the desk before him, the ball was in my court.

'Only if they were bright enough.'

'Exactly. Bright enough and late. Now that brings me to the point of this little chat. I am sure you are aware that the county allows boys, provided they reach the requisite academic standard, to transfer at sixteen to their local grammar school.'

I nodded, recalling one in particular.

'Well, over the summer recess – I do not think of them as holidays, less a rest from our labours, more a preparation of things to come – over the summer I visited County Hall and undertook some research. Have you ever seen the record office at County Hall?'

I shook my head. As far as I could remember, I'd never been near the place.

'Very impressive. Very impressive indeed. A complete record of every child's educational progress from infants to university. And do you know what I discovered?' More head-shaking. 'Well I'll tell you. In all the years that boys have been transferring at sixteen to the various grammar schools in the county, there has never been more than five from any one secondary modern school in any one academic year.'

I felt I ought to offer some response and suggested it showed that there weren't that many boys who developed late.

'On the contrary,' came the triumphant reply, 'it shows they haven't been allowed to develop.'

The serried ranks of Lower Five Gardening flashed across my mind's eye.

'My ambition' – he sat back in his chair and gave me one of those looks the First World War officers give to their men in films entitled *The Glorious Few* – 'is for Shothurst to beat that record.' At this point he leant forward and conspiratorially lowered his voice. 'I've analysed the numbers and after much thought I have selected ten boys who I consider to be of suitable quality and I intend to hive them off into a new and separate class which, to distinguish it from the other fifth-form classes, will be known as Upper Five Alpha.' I thought it best to nod in a thoughtful sort of manner. 'And this is where you come in. I want you to take them under your wing and give them a bit of a polish. The odd Latin epigram, that sort of thing.'

'*Carpe diem*, perhaps?'

'Exactly. *Carpe diem* or anything else you might think suitable. Let your learning and background, Balliol if I remember rightly, rub off on them. We, who have been entrusted with the torch of learning, must also 'stoop and build 'em up with worn-out tools'. Wouldn't you agree?'

In what turned out to be a pretty disreputable affair, the sole saving grace is that I took the job seriously. Much against his better judgement, I managed to squeeze ten wallet-files out of the school secretary (*Wallets is for Science, exercise books for English. They'll all be wanting one next*). With this piece of additional stationery, the chosen few were able to write their draft work in their exercise books before transcribing the final version on to file paper which in turn was to be kept in the wallet. The plan was to examine their wallet-files at regular intervals and enclose, suitably dated, a report on their progress or otherwise. Just before they left to take the exam, I would produce a final report to help their revision.

It was a couple of weeks later, after the necessary re-arrangements had taken place and I was on my way to *carpe* the *diem*, that the head took me to one side. 'Could I have a quick word with you? I have been having second thoughts about Dyson. I know he has the numbers to suggest he could cope but I am not sure he's really grammar school material. His father has found himself in trouble a couple of times. In fact, the whole family is a little... how should I put it... not from around here, if you catch me meaning. I'm not saying it's the boy's fault but maybe he'd be better served if pushed towards some useful apprenticeship. I demurred and pointed out, albeit in a slightly more subtle way, the more mud you chuck against the wall the more likely some of it would stick.

I was pleased when the head saw the force of my argument because in what was a relatively uninspiring if earnest group, Sid Dyson was the one pupil who stood out. Of course, his name wasn't really Sid. I'm sure his mother had a loftier ambition, but at some point in his life he must have picked up the name in the way a child might pick up measles. Yet, despite this modesty of nomenclature, when it came to putting pen to paper Sid Dyson definitely had talent, admittedly an odd and somewhat perverse talent, but there again Sid Dyson was an odd and perverse boy.

In order to explain his peculiar skill, it is necessary to have an understanding of the then structure of the O-Level

English examination. In addition to a test of comprehension, there was a list of essay titles from which the candidate had to choose and then compose an appropriate response in five to eight hundred words. The titles set were mostly run of the mill – *A Walk in the Countryside, My Favourite Hobby*, etc. – but as often as not there was one that the examiners hoped would be more challenging. One such, I recall, was *Man: the destroyer*. This had been included, no doubt, in the hope that some more sensitive soul would write feelingly about the fate of the white rhino or the pollution of the Antarctic. If so, the examination board had not counted on Sid. His response to the challenge began, if I remember correctly: *'Man the destroyer!' bellowed the captain to his faithful crew* – and continued in an unremitting carnage of depth charges to destroy the entire German submarine fleet.

In most cases, I would have taken the pupil quietly to one side and explained the purpose and function of the colon, but in Sid's case I was not so sure, so I said nothing. As time passed and essays were written and handed in, my suspicions were confirmed. Sid's modus operandi was to scan through the titles until he eventually found one that he could turn on its head. It didn't always work but when it did the results, either comic or tragic, were always a delight to read. It was one such that I now held in my hand. I looked again at that peculiarly cramped handwriting and reread the opening sentence.

### The Do-It-Yourself Movement
### Sid Dyson

*Asbestos maybut did nowt for the Do-it-Yourself movement, but it certainly did for me Dad.*

Holding it up to what was left of the torchlight, I scanned through the rest of the closely written pages, at first remembering the outline then the detail. Tom, a recent school-leaver, has triumphantly saved enough money to buy a second-hand motorbike only to return home to discover his father has been rushed to hospital where a few weeks later he dies from mesothelioma. As his mother is too distraught, the seventeen-year-old has to deal with the funeral arrangements. The father's sudden death has left the family in dire financial straits and rather than his mother suffer the ignominy of a pauper's burial, Tom decides to do it himself.

Interwoven with the main story is the father's ambition to retire to the countryside (now Tom can contribute to the family budget, his father has opened a savings account to that end). Tom, therefore, sets his mind on a 'green' or 'woodland' burial. Despite his best efforts there are still expenses to pay and Tom has to sell his bike to a mate. He is, however, able to borrow it back for one last trip, transporting, as pillion passenger, the body bag containing his father from the morgue to the burial ground. The story ends as the strapped-together driver and passenger carefully make their way out of the noise and grime of the town into the peace of the countryside.

I try to make out my comment written in red ink faded to grey:

*The work has a clear and strong story line complemented by your authentic narrative voice. It treads the line between sentimentality and sensationalism with great skill. A fine piece of writing. Well done!*

For a moment I couldn't for the life of me think why it should be in my loft, then bit by bit I put the story together. Just before the troupe of Upper Five Alpha had left to revise for its forthcoming examinations, I had gathered them all together and amidst some words of general encouragement returned to each boy the folder containing his year's work. I seem to remember they bought me a packet of cigarettes in return. All were present except Sid who had not been seen for the past few days. Rumour had it that he had hitchhiked to Portugal to watch his team play in some European cup final or other but there again Sid was always the subject of such speculation and he might just as likely have gone fishing. I later met one of his classmates who told me that as a result he had been expelled and not allowed to take the exams after all. No doubt the headmaster saw it as a satisfactory outcome.

I was on the point of putting the folder in the bin with the rest of the rubbish when I was struck by a pang of conscience. I had made quite a thing of how important each individual folder was. How, containing their own thoughts, it represented them and that sort of stuff. If anyone had the right to throw Sid's folder on the rubbish heap, it was Sid. So, I tucked the folder under my arm and resolved to ring the school to see if they still had Dyson's address then post it on with some sort of apology.

And that, I suppose, would have been that. But a couple of days later there occurred one of those coincidences that make Dickens seem so incredible. The phone rang and once more Marjory had demanded my wife's attention.

'Jonathan Long here. How's tricks?' I was about to mention that they were no trickier than usual but my former literary agent wasn't listening. 'Now it's like this. I was wondering if you could help me out. You can? Good man. The situation is as follows. Chapman's have been in touch. They want to put together a collection of short stories that reflect the cultural and political mess the country seems to be in at the moment. North-south divide, the sort of flimflam the *Guardian* gets excited about. I thought some of your old stuff might fit the bill. Could you send me a couple so I can have another look at them? Soon as possible, old man. Chapman's want it up and running for their Christmas list.'

I didn't write political-social 'stuff', I was more an 'irony of fate' man if I was anything at all. Long must have got me mixed up with someone else. Then I thought of Sid's story. If anything fitted the bill of 'grim up north', then that would. Why not send it off and see what sort of reception it got? No point at this stage saying it was written by a sixteen-year-old kid. Long wouldn't even read the first page. No, let it stand on its own two feet and see how it went. Even if it led to nothing else, I'm sure Sid would be dead chuffed that it had been considered for publication. So, I typed out the manuscript, tidied up the spelling and punctuation, and sent it off with an appropriate letter of the 'perhaps you might like to consider this' variety.

Some weeks passed and, if I assumed anything, I suppose I assumed Sid's effort must have been binned. Then what appeared to be a hastily scribbled note arrived in the post.

*Apologies for the delay in replying. Busiest time of the year as I'm sure you're aware. Really liked The Do-it-Yourself Movement. You seem to have found a new voice. As did Chapman's editor. Didn't want to change a word and decided to use it as the lead story in the collection. They apparently have high hopes for Christmas. Well done! Jonathan.*

*P.S. Contractual details to follow.*

I reread the letter trying to decide what to do. By now it had probably gone to press. Chapman's wouldn't be happy to have to pulp an entire edition. And even if something could be salvaged, alterations made, they'd miss the Christmas deadline. I thought about trying the truth but it would sound so stupid. I'd come into possession of the story because some football team was playing in a suburb of Lisbon. In the end, I persuaded myself, it would most probably come to nothing. A few hundred stuffed in Christmas stockings. A short review in the *Observer*'s 'Other Fiction', then quietly moulder on some remainder list, forgotten in the brave new world of 1976. Let sleeping dogs lie seemed the best policy.

But as any reader of Dickens knows, matters do not work out like that. Long had managed to cobble together some pretty well-known authors, including Roger Condon, who – older readers might recall – was currently having his day in the sun. The collection was favourably received in the Sunday broadsheets and for a time the short story as art form became the subject of much discussion. Articles appeared in *Arts Today*. Radio Three put together a symposium headed up by Condon to which I was invited. Maupassant, Balzac and Chekhov were duly paraded as star witnesses to support the proposition that the short story was a more important prose form than the novel. A sudden vivid snapshot of the truth rather than a day spent traipsing around Dublin. There was even a mention on *Woman's Hour*. But eventually interest waned and neo-Marxist structuralism once more became the *cri du jour*.

Nevertheless, *The Do-It-Yourself Movement & Other Stories* did well enough to go to reprint and I always felt a guilty start when the half-year royalties, for what they were worth, fell through the letter box. There were times when I tried to persuade myself that it was the art not the author that mattered and that if I hadn't done what I'd done, the story would never have seen the light of day. But I knew that argument was specious, a self-justifying lie. As it turned out, it wasn't that long before the cheques stopped and I allowed myself to think about the consequences less and less. Occasionally, there would be a literary uproar when one author would accuse another of plagiarism and the panic would again flood into my mind. But after a few years I convinced myself that it was all water under the bridge and nothing would come of it. Even the local library had got rid of its sole copy. It was at that point, when I had assumed everything was more or less done and dusted, that the phone rang and Sid made his request.

I looked at the clock. Ten minutes to two. I must sort out how I am going to deal with the situation when it arises. *Suppose there are some similarities. But rewriting earlier attempts is common literary practice. Even Shakespeare didn't write anything entirely original.* The papers would have a field day with that.

Better a more conciliatory approach. *All an unfortunate mistake, trying to give you a leg up, agent pushed on unasked.* At least that was somewhere near the truth.

*It wasn't as though I'd made any real money out of it. Ten per cent divided between nine of us is about diddly-squat.* Perhaps, if he cut up rough, fifty quid might settle it.

But the one thing that really worried me, even if it would do no apparent harm, was having my words thrown back at me:

*... only you will write in this book and you will write what you think, what you believe, what you know. It is your world and, when I enter your world, it will be a privilege, not a right. As a visitor I will consider and try to appreciate...*

At two o'clock exactly I sensed rather than heard the knocker being lifted then rattled a couple of times against its plate. A young man whom I only half recognised stood there in anorak and jeans that had seen better days. 'Ah, Sid. Good to see you. It must be six, seven years?'

'Five, sir, and actually it's Richard. I was only Sid at school. You know how it is.'

'Of course, Richard. Stupid of me. Well come in. Come in out of the cold.'

We walked in single file along the hall to what I called my study and after closing the door I gesticulated in the direction of the more comfortable chair. But Sid, Richard, went over to the bookshelves that covered two of the four walls of the room. After a moment or two it was clear he was looking for something in particular. Perhaps I should have sorted the matter there and then, but before I could say *I think I know what you're looking for* he shook his head, turned and walked back towards the chair.

'You've got a lot of books, sir, but I suppose you would have. Tools of the trade, so to speak.'

'Yes, I suppose I've collected quite a few over the years. Come on, sit down and tell me what I can do for you.'

Sid, for he would never be Richard, took a moment or two then perched somewhat uncomfortably on the edge of the seat. 'As a matter of fact, I *was* looking for something. It's about a book that I've come to see you. I thought I might be able to spot it in your shelves.' He tried to make himself more comfortable in the chair. 'It's like this. You remember in class you used to read us some short stories? Well, I know it sounds a bit silly but I would like to read them for myself. The trouble is I can't remember what they were called or even who wrote them. The one I was looking for was about a lad at borstal who deliberately lost a race.'

'Ah yes, Alan Sillitoe, "The Loneliness of the Long-

Distance Runner". You liked that, did you? Can't say it surprises me.'

'I remember how you explained to us it wasn't really about running. More about honesty and how honesty can mean different things to different people. Well, the thing is, sir, I would like to read it again to try to understand it properly. And some of the other stories you read, but I'm not sure how to go about it. I mean, I can't just go into the library and ask to borrow a book about two boys and a balloon, can I? So, I was wondering, if it wasn't too much trouble, if you could write out a list to get me started?'

'Of course I will. No problem, no problem at all.'

'You see, I brought this. Sid pulled out of his pocket a rather creased envelope and put it on my desk. 'It's stamped and everything. If you could put your list in it and drop it in the post. But only when you have time.' His voice faded away at the end of the sentence.

I stood up. 'I'll see to it as soon as I can. No, look, I'll do better than that.' I walked over to one of the bookshelves and pulled out a copy of the Sillitoe short stories. 'Here, take this to be getting along with.' I saw doubt in his face. 'No problem. Take it. I'm pretty sure I've got another copy somewhere. Probably stole it from Shothurst, if the truth be told.'

He smiled, seemed to be about to say something then changed his mind and said nothing. And that seemed to be that. I moved towards the door and, once more in single file, we walked down the hall. I opened the front door and held out my hand.

'Nice to see you again, Richard. If there's anything else I can help you with, you know where to find me.'

'Well, sir, there is one other thing. As a matter of fact,

it's why I really came to see you.' He paused as if trying to get his thoughts in order. 'It's all a bit awkward really. You remember when you used to teach me, you said I had some sort of talent at English, at writing and stuff like that? There was one time you hadn't handed my homework back and asked me to see you at the end of the lesson. I thought I was in for a twatting or a detention at best. I think the one you liked was about the lad who buried his dad. I don't suppose you remember it. Except you did say you might publish it.'

I didn't say that. What was he talking about?

'You must remember, sir. In the school mag you started – *Shot in the Dark.*'

'Of course, I remember. Completely forgotten about it. Don't expect the old mag's still going after all these years.'

'Well, that's what I came to see you about. I've got quite a serious question to ask and it would mean quite a lot to me if you gave me an honest answer.'

I suppose it was at this moment I realised that the only way was indeed to be honest. I might not have meant to do it, but do it I did and was about to ask Sid to come back into the house when it all came out in a bit of a rush.

'The truth is I'm fed up working at Macey's. What I really need is something that offers a bit more of a challenge. So I've decided to go back to studying and, maybe, if I get all the right qualifications, get a job as an English teacher. What I really want to know, sir, is whether you think I've any chance of making the grade.'

## ANABASIS

Smoke. Of course, that was it. There was no longer a smell of smoke. The last time I had stood at the station waiting for Dave, the Beeching Axe was still in the process of working its way north and the various branch lines that trickled in from the surrounding pit villages continued to function. In those days, Dave lived at the end of a minor tributary and, even then, back in the fifties, passenger trains from these verges of civilisation were in short supply. Now, of course, there are none. But on the day that mattered there used to be two and one of them, as luck would have it, arrived just after 2 p.m. I would wait while two carriages pulled by an ageing G5 shuffled into Platform 4A. Where, with an apparent exhalation of relief, it disgorged its bescarved passengers before leaving the station to huff and grumble in a weed-infested siding while awaiting their return. The 'day that mattered' was Saturday or, to be precise, every other Saturday, when Dave and I would turn up to watch 'the lads'. To kick every ball. To share the hope and despair. Today, almost half a lifetime later, I once more waited for Dave.

But on this occasion I stood on Platform 1 to meet the London train. Unlike the G5's more modest approach, you heard the wail of its attention-demanding siren long before it came into view. Then, after a suitably dramatic pause, a silent torpedo glided out of the tunnel applying noiseless brakes to come to rest with neither apparent effort nor unnecessary fuss. After another theatrical moment the automatic doors slid to one side and the passengers scampered towards the station exit as if about to witness some momentous event. As the crowd thinned, I found I no longer had to crane my neck in my attempt to spot Dave and I was trying to reassure myself that I couldn't have missed him or met the wrong train when I heard my name called. I'd been looking the wrong way. Of course, he would be travelling first class. I waved and shouted something back. Dave approached, changed his grip on his overnight bag and extended a hand. 'Good to see you. It's been a long time.' He had changed and not changed, Dave McFetrich, bright grammar school boy, unanimously voted Most Likely To Succeed, heralded by the press, saviour of the City. 'You know, you haven't changed a bit. It must be nearly twenty years. Still pushing the pen, are you?' The unspoken answers were – yes, nearer twenty-five, after a fashion. 'Right, I'll dump this in left luggage and we'll be off then.'

'Off' was to the old ground. Once, with its double-decker stands, it had been the envy of the Football League, but gradually decay had set in. Now that a new breed of spectators had demanded better facilities and the accountants had realised there was money to be made out of corporate hospitality and an on-site club shop, telephone calls had been made and demolition experts consulted. I might have been persuaded that you've got to move with the times if the Board had gone about it the right way. Of course, demolish the bits that were getting on for eighty years old and provide proper facilities, but employ an architect that is in touch with the history and tradition built over so many generations. Have a few hospitality boxes by all means but make certain you retain the feel of the place.

But. Oh no. The bean-counters clearly held the stage. The plan was to move the new stadium out of town on to some soulless industrial estate and develop the old ground into a housing estate or a Tesco hypermarket or something. To add insult to injury, their main reason for the change seemed to be that parking would be easier. That missed the whole point. Sitting in a traffic jam. That isn't going to the match. You might just as well have been taking the missus to IKEA. Right-thinking supporters were up in arms and old wounds were reopened when it was rumoured that an unnamed German car company were not only going to set up a factory nearby but were to sponsor the ground. The Stadium of Vorsprung durch Technik!

Protest groups were set up. Committees formed. For some reason I found myself chairing an action group and soon discovered the limitations of the democratic will. Most debates generated more heat than light and as the due date approached, the suggestions – from boycotting the home games to buying the ground and refounding the club – grew more and more absurd. Eventually I tired of waiting for something constructive to happen and resigned. Perhaps if Dave had still been with us, matters might have been handled differently.

Funnily enough it must have been around this time that I received my first-ever letter from Dave, saying that sometime in the near future he would have to be going up north. Apparently, he had some local business to attend to. He could easily break his journey and would like to have one last look at the old ground before it disappeared altogether. Was I up for it? Have a look around and maybe pick up the odd souvenir (a turnstile for his office door had been my original and somewhat cynical reaction), but secretly I had been pleased. Most of the old crowd had moved on. It would be good to be back in the loop, if only for an afternoon. Bumped into Dave McFetrich the other day. Yes, that's right, *the* Dave McFetrich. It seems he's up for a knighthood. Of course, he didn't say as much, but we, Dave and me, go back a long way. The moment had now come. He deposited his pigskin overnight bag in left luggage and our personal anabasis (if I've dredged up the right word from a somewhat patchy classical education) began. We left the station before turning into the high street to cross the bridge over the river that divided the town.

On match days, this had caused a bottleneck to rival most bottlenecks. During the latter part of the morning the council estates on the southern reaches of the town slowly emptied themselves of their male occupants. This steady stream headed north, merging with the outspillings of older wynds, streets and terraces, to be finally swollen by those earlier arrivals who had already set off to enjoy a euphemistic 'swift half'. This ever-increasing surge, rolling through the town like some benign tidal wave, swept towards the bridge. Pedestrians who on any other day of the week kept respectfully to the pavements now spread shoulder to shoulder across all four carriageways. For an hour they knew they were the masters. No bus, car or bike dared take them on. Only the occasional tram, trapped between iron rails and its overhead pantograph, tried to push its way through the ever-mounting drift of humanity.

Twenty, or to be precise twenty-three, years ago I lived on the north side of the river and had had no apparent reason to go anywhere near the bridge on my way to the match, but meeting Dave as he got off the 2.07 was an essential part of the ritual. We needed time before kick-off to discuss selection and injuries, not to mention the opponents' supposed strengths and weaknesses, and then – then, there was always the question of Harry. When it came to football, Harry was never far from our thoughts and on match day he held centre stage. He was our star player. When Harry played well, the team played well and, more often than not, won. But with Harry it wasn't a matter of form. He could always play well when he wanted to. When he didn't want to, he played the fool. One of my earliest football memories was of our star inside forward requisitioning an umbrella from a spectator to protect himself from a sudden cloudburst, then holding it aloft while continuing to play with his normal aplomb. (It might be relevant, at this point, to mention that Harry did nothing so crude as to allow the ball to hit his head.) On another occasion, frustrated that none of his teammates had moved into the spaces he had just created, he stopped, gave a shrug and sat on the ball. The match came to a halt. The away side also stopped, suspecting they were about to be made fools of. The home side, as if in sympathy, stopped and tried to fathom out what to do next. The referee, confused as to the legality of Harry's behaviour, decided to blow his whistle for half-time.

Mostly, the crowd loved him. We knew he would try when it really mattered. Especially against those stuck-up London teams. We also wanted to believe that, with these acts of rebellion, he was somehow striking a blow for all of us. A symbolic mocking of those club directors and their ilk who determined our subsistence-level rates of pay, sold us shoddy goods with a 500 per cent mark-up and sent in the bailiffs if we fell in arrears by as little as two bob a week. There were those with a more puritanical streak who thought he was a show-off and should get on with what he was paid for, but even the most begrudging of us would be forced to forgive him because of one piece of on-pitch magic. Because of 'the trick'. Others tried and failed to accomplish it. Physicists deemed it impossible. But Harry could and did accomplish the apparent impossible. Not so often for it to become commonplace or so infrequently that it might be considered a fluke. 'The trick' was simple. If the ball was passed to him with sufficient speed and at the appropriate angle, Harry would stub his boot at the exact point where leather and grass met. The ball flew upwards, apparently out of control, causing the defender to lunge towards it in grateful expectation. But when the ball landed, instead of bouncing forward as nature intended, it seemed to bite into the ground, momentarily pause, then roll back to its master. From a footballing point of view there was little to gain from it. From a psychological point of view it turned defenders into dithering incompetents. We loved 'the trick'. It belonged to us. It was our bit of magic that separated us from the rest.

But today the bridge was once more its usual car-infested highway. Pedestrians, pushed to the periphery, could look down on the absence of cranes that had once lined the shipyards and remember the day when this had been the biggest shipbuilding town in the world. The forges that specialised in rudders and propeller blades were still there. Now no longer spitting fire and brimstone but converted into EU-funded museums dressed up as theme parks. Today Dave and

I walked the same streets we had walked two decades ago. Once, before the arrival of cut-price stores, there had been an amalgam of greengrocers, butchers, bakeries and bookshops and, sandwiched between a cobbler and a chippie, a second-hand record store where I would sift through the 78s, hoping to find a Johnny Dodds, Jelly Roll Morton or early Charlie Parker. Now there was nothing but bookies, pawnshops and the inevitable derelict pub.

Today, as always, we walked along the same side of the road, on the same pavements, no doubt avoiding the same cracks, crossing at the same point as we always did to turn into Pym Street and get our first view of the ground, or rather the edge of the stand and the sign above Gate 7A. Here we would join the shuffling queue pushing through the turnstile before making our way to stand in front of the same crush barrier. But now the stand had gone and in its place was an extensive billboard showing, against the background of a window-sparkling semi-detached house, Mother, immaculately dressed, secateurs in a garden-gloved hand hovering over a rose bush; a blond-haired boy throwing a beach ball to his little sister; and Father doing something technical to the car in the drive. Here the sun was always shining, the grass always green. This is what you aimed for. This is the dream.

Dave, rather fastidiously, kicked to one side a bit of timber that might once have been part of a door. 'It looks as if the rehabilitation came not a moment too soon.' I didn't answer. I was looking at his shoes. I'd never noticed them before. I remember my mother saying you can always judge a man by his shoes. Yes, Dave had gone up in the world. Thinking back, I suppose I was a bit shocked. Of course, he was right. You've got to move with the times, but there was such a thing as respect for the departed. At the time, though, I nodded in apparent agreement, adding, 'At least, we won't have to climb in today.'

He smiled at the memory. The FA Cup sixth round against the league leaders, champions of Europe, darling of the Press, for the rest of us a variety of invective. In the first game we had frittered away a two-goal lead. 3–1 up with five minutes to go. (*Still there's always the replay. We've got a good chance at home.*) I remember it was a cold Tuesday night. I'd forgotten my gloves and Dave was late. 'Sorry, had to help my dad shift some furniture.' We hurried through streets unusually empty towards the anxious buzz of the crowd. Suddenly a crescendo of noise. The teams were out. No time to look for Gate 7. Any gate would do. We reached the back street that separated a rundown terrace from the rear of the ground. The first gate we came to was shuttered and locked. And the second and third. A small group slouched around as if uncertain what to do next. Starting to run, we pushed passed them, making for the Paddock. 'No point, mate. They're all shut. Ground full half an hour ago.'

We had watched every home game, come rain, sleet or hail, and now we were going to miss the one that really mattered. But Dave kept on running. 'The Gents, the Gents, come on!' What the fuck was he talking about? Then I realised. Surrounding the ground was a fifteen-foot wooden palisade, but in each corner the wood turned to brick. These were the outer walls of the Gents toilets, a refuge for the incontinent, if they could stomach the stench. But they could yet be our saviour. Here the height of the perimeter fence dropped from fifteen to nine or ten feet. A couple of steps back, one foot pushing down on the wall to gather upward momentum, arms outstretched, ignoring the cemented pieces of broken glass, to pull up and over to drop into the Stygian depths beneath. We were in – after a fashion. In fact, for all our efforts, we had only reached the concourse that encircled the ground proper. The back of the Popular End loomed out of the gloom. No doubt to save money it had been built on a slag heap, with the side facing the pitch tiered with reinforced concrete. Its rear remained a not-too-steep slope of compressed cinder and stone. No problem. As we scrabbled our way up, I became aware of other shadowy figures, scarcely substantial ghosts, the warm air of their breath made solid by the cold mist blowing in from the sea. We reached the top, straddled the low safety fence and squeezed our way into the upper edge of the crowd. Despite the crush I was able to filch out my handkerchief and wrap it round the fleshy part just below the thumb, before wedging the hand into my coat pocket. It would soon stop bleeding in this temperature.

On all my previous visits I had never seen the ground from this angle. It was like being perched on the rim of a bowl filled with light. At its bottom lay an almost empty green space surrounded by tier upon tier of humanity. Every inch of every section of every stand was beyond bulging point, scores of fans, mostly children, had spilled out on to the area that separated the crowd from the touchline. They sat on the grass ten-deep, arms clasped around drawn-up knees while a defender tried to manoeuvre a space to allow him to take a throw-in. And the noise. Not the usual Saturday afternoon mixture of encouragement and abuse. More a roar of aggressive defiance that rose and fell to reflect the state of play.

And then it happened. One of our midfielders, motivated more by wishful thinking than intent, lofted the ball towards the opposition's penalty area. The sort of hoof-and-hope pass that hangs in the air long enough for the defence to compose itself and ninety-nine times out of a hundred nullify any threat. But on the hundredth occasion it will fall to the one man who can threaten the rule. And on this occasion, it did. Harry must have made his mind up in a fraction of a second, or perhaps he didn't think, perhaps he just knew. As the ball, still in the air, reached his outstretched foot, he leant back slightly and with his right instep flicked the ball to shoulder height and an arm's length from his body. While gravity took its course he changed shape by pivoting on a slightly bent right leg then sweeping his left leg to volley the ball goalward. Such was the precision of the shot and the stillness of his head, a small puff of whitewash leapt in the air as the ball struck the juncture of goal line and post. The best goalkeeper in England (and in those days that meant the best goalkeeper in the world) hadn't taken as much as a step or half raised an arm.

And for another fraction of a second there was complete silence as if what we had seen was some trick of the light and the ball had, in reality, passed outside the upright. But as that fraction broke, so did the torrent. In the crush, all limbs were trapped and the only bodily part left to express their joy was their mouths. The noise built, gaining momentum and volume, before cascading down from the packed terraces like some uncontrollable wave. Then I too seemed to be part of the wave, a rudderless boat, swept first right, then left, but always down, my feet scarcely touching the ground, passing faces contorted with pain and alarm. And then the wave ebbed, breath was exhaled and movement slowed. Confused, I tried to get my bearings. Somehow I'd been plucked from the top right-hand corner of the terracing and now stood shaking with both fear and exhilaration at the bottom left. Of Dave there was no sign.

No, there was no need to climb in, not today. Just step around the rubble which had once supported ten thousand people, picking your way through lumps of concrete and pieces of distorted metal. There was not much left to see. A patch of mutilated grass that had once been a penalty area, enough space for a dozen kids to patch together a game. Each tried, as kids do, to monopolise possession, deaf to demands to pass it to a teammate. But there was one lad who stood out. He was skinnier than the others, oversize shorts dangling below his knees, socks round his ankles. Whereas the others had shirts with the name and number of their hero emblazoned on their backs, he wore a rather faded jumper that looked as if it had been washed once too often. But it wasn't just his appearance that made him different. The others, head down, tried to keep the ball at their feet rushing hither and thither in a game of their own, yet he played head up, with the air of someone about to do something significant. The ball suddenly broke loose and flew in his direction. As it landed, he stubbed his foot at the point where ball and grass met. The ball rose, landed and started to roll. 'Did you see that?' I grabbed Dave's arm. 'I was sure it was going to...' But the game had already stopped. Like a gathering of small birds that have seen the shadow of a raptor, the players had slipped away. Only the owner of the ball had momentarily paused to retrieve his prized possession. We half turned to see what had so startled the flock. Some temporary custodian of the wreck had appeared shouting and waving his arms. The children continued to retreat until, safely out of range, they felt sufficiently confident to offer some advice of their own.

*Bloody kids*. We both turned to look at him and said nothing. *It's for their own good*. His tone grew to a crescendo of anxious defiance. *It's not safe. It's not safe to play here. Bloody kids.* We still said nothing. He muttered something indistinguishable under his breath and turned back to his hut. There was really not much more we could do. I picked up a divot of grass that might or might not have been the penalty spot, looked at it for a moment, then tossed it away. Dave seemed more preoccupied with the site map pinned to the advertising hoarding than searching for souvenirs. 'Oh good! In the end they *have* named a street after him.' We stopped for a moment to have a last look. Dave took a notebook out of his jacket pocket and running his finger down the plan made a series of entries before taking a couple of steps to one side so he could see the whole length of the old ground. Apparently satisfied, he returned in a more cheerful mood and took me by the elbow. 'Come on. There's always the Grapes.'

A drink in the Fox and Grapes had traditionally been the last act of our Saturday afternoon routine. Dave had time to kill before his next and last train to the other side of nowhere and I, if the truth be told, had little better to do. So it had been our habit to repair to the taproom, shoulder our way to the bar and mull over the triumphs and disasters of the last couple of hours. Drinks finished, we would walk a few yards together until we reached the corner of Pym Street and Cromwell Road. Here, before going our separate ways, we would pause as though trying to keep the moment afloat.

'See you in a couple of weeks, then?'

'Sure, a week Saturday. Have to go or I'll miss my train.'

But long before we were in sight of the corner where those two great parliamentarians collided, I realised something was wrong. The building still existed. The Grapes did not. In its place stood 'Executive Apartments for Sale or Let'. We looked at it for a moment or two. The architect, no doubt a student of the school of shabby chic, had retained a few of the original features. I noticed, in particular, the stained-glass windows depicting Aesop's admonitory tale.

'Well, it wasn't much of a place, really.'

There was a moment or two of awkward silence. Dave looked at his watch. 'I must dash. I've really got to catch the next train. Look, take this.' He fumbled once again in his pocket. 'If you're ever in town, this number should find me.' I took the card, flipping it over to see the elaborately embossed lettering:

*David J. McFetrich F.R.S.S.I.*
*Regional Property Development*

I looked up. He had already reached the main road and half turned towards me.

'We must do this again sometime.'

I nodded and raised a hand in acknowledgement, but we both knew we wouldn't.

## THE GIRL ON THE TRAIN

The pull up to the top of the ridge was longer than it looked and I had crossed a number of false summits before I could stand on the watershed proper and look at the scene that dropped beneath my feet. The path continued, now more steeply, wending its way downhill to the sea loch and the building where I intended to spend the night. Good! No smoke. There was a chance it would be unoccupied.

Once I had given up any real thoughts about writing, I'd taken to filling up my spare time by wandering the hills, stopping when it suited me, sleeping wherever I could get my head down. At first there were very few of us, but as the Sunday supplements, spurred on by commercial interests, exalted the joys of the 'outdoor experience', so numbers increased, first in ones and twos, then in gangs, all bobble hats and inappropriate coloured clothing, mistaking buzzards for eagles, commandeering bothies and complaining about the lack of amenities. So, as this new wave of invaders sped up the motorways, I, like the Celts before me, was forced to retreat further into what was left of the wildness to find the peace and quiet only isolation can bring.

I was part way through a round trip that was fast becoming a favourite. Sleeper to Fort William. Leave the Mallaig train at Glenfinnan. Cross to and through the Rough Bounds of Knoydart. Boat across Loch Nevis. Steamer up the Sound of Sleat to the Kyle of Lochalsh. Take, leave and rejoin the train to Inverness, leapfrogging stations with trips into the interior. Then finally, Inverness and the express train home. So far all had gone well. Almost too well to be true. A lump of high pressure had parked itself somewhere around Rockall forcing any Atlantic cloud south of the Highlands. I had climbed the hills I wanted to climb, visited the places I wanted to visit. To cap it all I had the bothy and the sunset to myself. All was – I was going to say perfection, but there must be a better word, a word that describes a sense of excited contentment – but if there is, I can't put my finger on it. Suffice to say it was a time when landscape and self were at one and all was as well as I thought it could ever be.

Next day after a leisurely sail up the Sleat, I arrived at Kyle in time to stock up on food and have my first pint of the trip. It was the usual soulless Highland bar, floored in cracked lino and offering unnecessarily cold keg beer. The only attempt to alleviate the overall drabness was a large mahogany specimen case that had been mounted on one of the walls. Within, wings outspread in the characteristic W formation, was a stuffed gannet. I couldn't take my eyes off it. There was something disturbing about all that power and freedom of movement being trapped in a glass case and it didn't take me long to decide that rather than sit there drinking in the gloom, I'd prefer to stand on the platform and wait.

The one advantage of being first on the train is you can choose where to sit. A seat with a table and with your back to the engine. Much better to watch the view slowly receding than a bewilderment of objects rushing towards you. Somewhere a whistle blew. The carriages momentarily lurched against their coupling before settling into a gently accelerating forward movement. That's good. I'll have the table to myself. Plenty of room to finish my sandwich, spread out the map and reacquaint myself with the route to the next bothy.

'Excuse me. Is that seat taken?'

I looked up. There are some women whom I find immediately appealing, something that marks them out. I'm not sure what – the lift of the chin, the poise that only complete physical control can bring, moving without apparent movement. As I say, I'm not even sure what I mean let alone find the words to describe it – describe them? But there's one thing I'm certain of – when they smile, they also smile with their eyes. Her free hand, half raised in the direction of the seat opposite, was still silently repeating the question. Much shuffling of maps and a half-eaten sandwich.

'Of course. I mean of course not.'

'Thank you. I only just made it.' She placed her bag next to the window, scrupulously restricting herself to the allotted space. 'Are you sure it's all right? You seem terribly busy.' She looked anxiously around the carriage. 'I didn't mean to disturb you. I could always move.'

'No, no. Please don't. It would be nice to have someone to talk to. To share this.' There was a moment when my hand, that was supposed to be gesticulating at the sequestered loch, hovered over the remnants of lettuce, tomato and cheese. A slight raising of an eyebrow. 'No, sorry, not the sandwich. The view.'

She smiled, brushed what might have been a crumb from her seat before settling into her place across the table.

'Well, aren't you going to?'

'Sorry. Going to what?'

'Talk. You said it would be nice to talk.'

'Ah, the view. Well it seems to have disappeared.'

'Has it?' She looked out of the window at what was now the side of a nondescript cutting. 'So it has. Never mind. Anyway, I had rather hoped you might tell me what you are doing here. In Scotland. On this train. People are always more interesting than places. Don't you think?'

I was in the middle of a rather rambling account of my movements over the previous few days when I noticed an increasingly puzzled expression which suddenly changed to a smile of apparent comprehension. 'Oh, you're one of those, what do you call them, hill-catchers, no, I've got it, peak-baggers. You have lists, don't you, that you tick off? A bit like train-spotters.'

Was that a serious question or just a joke? What was obviously needed was some witty riposte but none came to mind and the best I could manage was to mutter something about to travel hopefully was often better than to arrive. She seemed to think about this for some time before replying, 'Yes, I agree. Rather like Christmas, I suppose. It's very rare you get exactly what you hoped for.'

It was at this point the train entered a tunnel which effectively stopped the conversation but by glancing into the darkened glass of the window I was able to look more carefully at my travelling companion. She was past the age when she could have been called pretty though no doubt at one time she would have been described as such. But certainly attractive, not as in the damning with faint praise sense, but attractive as in magnetic. There was certainly something about her that held your attention, and the more I looked the surer I was that I had seen her before. I suddenly sensed she had noticed me watching her, and to cover my confusion I flattened out the map in an apparently businesslike way.

And that seemed to be that. She moved her bag back to her lap and carefully rifled through the contents until she found what she was looking for. She looked up and smiled then started to read. Most people who read tend to slouch in a slightly hunched position, sit sideways in the chair allowing the muscles, and the limbs they control, to flop somewhat. But not her. Back straight, head perfectly still, text held at an optician's length from her eyes. The lack of movement gave the impression of a person floating rather than being buffeted by the reality of a swaying train.

I've no idea why – perhaps it was her particular kind of beauty that had reminded me of something or someone – but before I knew it the words had irretrievably escaped.

'Have you ever acted in pantomime?'

Her eyes lifted over the top of the book. 'Whom did you have in mind? Mother Goose?'

'No, of course not. I'm sorry, it was a stupid question.'

'It's never the question that's stupid. In fact, it could be said that questions are anything but stupid. Risky, perhaps, but never stupid. Wouldn't you agree?'

Once more, I was left casting around for some suitable reply when the tunnel ended with a sudden whoosh of air. The next stop was mine. At least, that was the station I had intended to stop at. For a moment I was tempted to stay on. Wait until it was her turn to alight and pretend it was also my stop. But that seemed a pretty stupid thing to do. No point in compounding my foolishness. Nevertheless, when the moment came, I deliberately alighted uptrain of the station's exit. I wanted to watch her reaction, if any, as her window passed me. I stopped and fiddled with the strapping on my rucksack. No, buried in a book. No more than passing the time. But then at the very moment when she was disappearing from view, I thought she looked up and half nodded. Before I had the chance to respond she was gone and I was left watching the red tail light fading as it curved out of sight.

It was all very odd. It was just a girl on a train. But the smile – that was hard to pin down. Friendly? Yes. But there was something more than that. Encouraging? Most probably not. Wishful thinking on my part. Anyway she's gone and I've got to make the bothy before it gets too dark to sort the maps and plan the next move. Yet as I walked up the forestry track, it wasn't the possibilities of the morrow but the past opportunities of today that continued to occupy my thoughts. It was as though there was something on the edge of my mind that kept trying to nudge its way in. Oh well, try to think of something else. Settle into a steady rhythm. Concentrate on planning tomorrow's expedition. The first bit over the river could be quite tricky.

Of course, switching off usually does it and suddenly it came to me. It was nothing to do with pantomimes. It was the same poise I had glimpsed in my local quite a long time ago. The pub stood, as is so often the case, opposite the parish church, forming a convenient meeting place for groom, best man and assorted hangers-on. For obvious reasons the appearance of a group dressed up to the nines compares more than favourably with the average Saturday afternoon drinker, but even among the glamour she had stood out. She was not only strikingly beautiful but somehow she seemed – aloof would be the wrong word – seemed that she was with them, yet somehow beyond them, as if searching for something or someone that she knew had already vanished. I went to the bar for a refill but when I looked back, she had disappeared. The funny thing was that the door which normally swung to on a particularly vicious spring must have jammed for it had failed to fully close. It was as if someone had slipped out, inviting another to follow. It was that sense of other-worldliness that I tried to recapture in a short story I had submitted for publication. It didn't get anywhere and by now I'd forgotten the detail but there was something about it that seemed somehow relevant. The opening sentence perhaps. I usually took care over those. Or there again, perhaps not.

Perhaps instead of just wondering, I should have stayed on the train. At least find out why she was in this part of Scotland. Did she live here? On holiday? We might have had quite a lot in common. Come on! What on earth are you drivelling about? Acting like a sixteen-year-old. Just think for a moment. What would have happened if you had stayed on until it was her stop and got off with her? What then? A polite *Good night* before she disappeared into the gloaming or, even worse, was met by her husband. *I'm sorry I can't introduce you. I'm afraid I don't know your name.* And anyway, what would you have done if she had just stood there waiting for you to make the next move? Either way, it would be another fine mess you'd have gotten yourself into – though in all probability less Lawrence than Hardy. Forget about the whole thing. Hit the sack. Have an early start and get back in the groove. Mind you, there was still some connection between her and that story I'd written that continued to rankle.

It was probably the sight of the bothy that calmed things down. Of all the unlocked shelters I have used, this is my favourite. Not for the view – it is stuck in the middle of a wood of uniform pine. Nor for the amenities – it was little more than a glorified shed – but for its location. Any estate agent with a hill-going clientele would enthuse on this particular merit. Hills on the doorstep, twenty minutes downhill to the nearest train station and once on the train the world's your oyster. You can alight and rejoin wherever you like with excursions into the fastnesses of Torridon and Applecross at your beck and call. I often wondered what the suit and briefcase brigade made of the somewhat dishevelled figure that seemed to have nothing better to do than get on and off their train as they commuted to and from work.

After a good night's sleep and an even better day on the hill, equilibrium of mind and body had reasserted itself. The summits I had reached were relatively lowly hills by Highland standards, but their distinct separateness gave them a sense of independence that chimed with my current state of being. Although the descent had been steep with its usual quota of loose rock and ankle-wrenching tufts of grass, I was making good progress. Certainly, good enough to reach the station hotel with sufficient time to get something to eat and drink without having to bolt it down. As I reached the lower slopes, I saw the eastbound train arrive and by the time I had reached the hotel, I had to pick my way through a pile of carelessly dumped backpacks. Eventually reaching the bar, I half waved a fiver to try to catch the barman's attention. I had just been served when over the general hubbub...

'I knew you'd stop here.'

I turned round and there she was – the girl on the train. For some reason I felt guilty as though I had been caught out in some way. Come on. Think of something to say. You wanted the opportunity and here it is – no strings attached.

'Hello again. How did the book finish up?'

'The bad, unhappily. The good, unluckily.'

'Right,' I called over the mass of humanity. 'Can I buy you a drink?'

'Thank you. A malt, please. Glen Briddoch if they've got it.' She started to sort out something in her bag.

'No problem, small or large?'

'Just a large.' She looked up from her sorting and smiled. 'That is, without water.'

I returned to the bar still clutching my untouched pint, bought the whisky and balanced my way back to the table. Whereas the earlier part of the trip had seemed a continuous stream of well-being, now everything seemed to be happening in confusingly disjointed chunks.

She watched me trying, not very successfully, to do a juggling act with whisky and daysack in one hand and a pint in the other then, with the minimum of fuss, she reached across and, removing the beer from my hand, placed the glass precisely in the middle of a drip mat. I hovered, uncertain as to my next move.

'I'm afraid I can't stay long, but please sit down.' She moved a foot or so along the bench to make room. 'I'm glad I caught you. Are you, by any chance, thinking of climbing Craig Coire nan Lochan tomorrow?'

How on earth did she know that? Of course, the map. I had been looking at it when she boarded the train. But it was odd she should pick the very hill I had my eye on. 'Yes, as a matter of fact, that was the plan.' 'Oh good, I was wondering if I might be part of the plan and come with you.'

I thought for a moment. There could be no harm in that. 'Yes, of course. I'd be more than happy. Nice to have company for a change. Would you want us to meet here?'

'No. I wouldn't be able to do that. I assume you will start up on the track by the lodge. If you look at your map, you'll see a shieling marked on the edge of the wood, just after the first bend. I'll meet you there. That is if you're sure I can come.'

'Sure I'm sure. It would be a pleasure. Could you excuse me a moment, if I nip to the Gents. I'll be right back. We can sort out times and other details then.' I was as quick as the circumstances permitted but when I returned, the glass and the bench were empty.

It was only when the ground steepened that I realised I was walking faster than usual. Typical, always rushed it when anxious. Even as a child I'd realised the pain was in the waiting. If something was going to go wrong, best get it over and done with. On the hill, especially in mist, my hurry was to check my navigation, anxious to find if the line on the map turns up as the expected boundary fence on the ground. Once found, the self-confidence floods back. The stride slackens, the lungs gently expel air. It is an insecure line that splits hope and fear. What happens if she is not there? Should I wait or just carry on? I was beginning to think that I had set myself up for some fool's errand.

I needn't have worried. As soon as the ground began to fall back I could see the shieling and a figure poised beside it. The sun must have been behind me for, as I appeared, her body stiffened and a hand was raised against the glare. I waved and hurried on.

'Hello! You're early.'

I looked at my watch – I *must* have walked quickly.

'Right. If you're still up for it, we better get going. I can't really afford to miss the early evening train.'

She turned her head to look at the hill. Wisps of mist had

started to cling to the summit. 'You should be all right. Not that far and not too much uphill. Should have plenty of time to make your connection.' I watched her carefully as she picked up her daysack. Good-quality cagoule if somewhat on the bright side, sensible trousers. Proper boots. Good. Looks as though she knows what she's doing. That was a relief. I didn't have time to mess about.

The lower slopes went easily enough and there was an edge to the wind to encourage brisk movement. Though the early morning sun was now covered in cloud, the summit was still relatively clear. At the mouth of the corrie I stopped to weigh up the lie of the land. The hillside in front of us was steep and seamed with outcrops of rock that might prove awkward but at its right-hand end was a rake slanting diagonally to join the summit ridge above all apparent difficulties.

'I think the rake would be the best bet.' I started to move in that direction

'Fine, if that's what you want. Mind you, straight up looks more interesting.'

As it turned out, the frontal assault would have proved easy enough and it was only on the final section of the ridge that we were confronted by an unavoidable step of rock some forty- or fifty-feet high. Fortunately, it wasn't a complete blank face but split by a deep gash as if some giant axe had tried to cleave it in half. Closer inspection showed that the gash was also fragmented – a rib of rock separated two steep but climbable gullies that rose from a surprisingly green grass platform. Of the two, the left-hand one looked the easier, at least at the start.

'I think we should try this one.'

She looked at the left branch then climbed a few feet up the right.

'This one looks more solid but you may be right. You'll soon find out.'

The gully was going easily enough at the start but after the first twenty feet or so, it suddenly steepened. It was difficult to judge how problematic it might prove but any difficulty would be certainly worsened by what looked like a lot of loose rock. Not a good place to make a mistake.

'Keep well back. There's some loose stuff up here. Don't start until I give you a shout.'

As is often the case, it wasn't as hard as it first looked and it was easy enough to either secure or avoid any dangerously poised bits of masonry. Going down, of course, would be a different matter. After the rock step, the gully fell back to an easier angle and I stopped to look back and see if she needed any help. I was surprised how quickly she followed me up the awkward step. More floating than climbing. Definitely not the rather clumsy heaving and thrutching methods I'd employed.

Eventually both branches converged at a curiously contorted piece of rock that formed a sort of pinnacle. Once past this obstacle, the ridge fell back and rose to what I assumed was the top. I say 'assumed' for while we'd been making our way up the gully the mist had started to thicken. At the moment it was still one of those in-and-out sort of affairs that causes little problem on the way up when all you have to do is follow the rising ground until the cairn finally appears. On the way down I needed to be sure where I was going and remember to be more careful. Particularly if the mist got worse.

'Well then, that's another one ticked off your list.'

Her remark rather took the gloss off reaching the summit. Back to the bobblies.

'I prefer not to think of it like that, but you're right. In weather like this it's rather like a dog peeing on a lamp-post. One thing's certain. There's little point in hanging about here.' I took out the compass from my cagoule pocket and started to check the back bearing. 'Better make sure we know what we're doing. If we're not careful we might end up in the wrong valley.'

'That might be fun.' I looked to see if she was joking but she seemed serious enough.

It's always a relief when you find out your compass isn't lying and what you expect to turn up, in fact does turn up. But on this occasion, I was doubly pleased when the twisted bit of rock appeared out of the gloom and I knew I had not only found the head of the gullies but showed a level of competence which I hoped would impress.

'Ladies first.' I gesticulated in mock courtesy at the branch of the gully we had previously ascended. I let her get a bit of a start and was about to follow when I remembered the loose rock. Probably more sensible if I looked at the other branch. It would certainly be safer and, with both of us moving together, probably save time. Halfway down I congratulated myself on making the right decision. The rock was solid and foot- and hand-holds appeared wherever they were necessary. I was down in what seemed like half the time it had taken me to get up. I lowered myself the last few feet on to the grass platform and called out into the mist. 'I'm down. You OK?' No answer. Well probably she couldn't hear me from here. I walked round the rock rib that separated the two gullies and called again. Still no answer. I climbed up a few feet to pass a kink in the gully that blocked the upward view. No sign of a soul. She seemed to have disappeared off the face of the earth.

My first feeling was one of annoyance. What on earth was she playing at? I had made it more than clear I couldn't afford to miss the 4.30. If I didn't connect with the Inverness sleeper, I'd have to stay overnight and my ticket would have expired. And that would mean explanations when I eventually got home. It wasn't as if I had done anything wrong but I knew from past experience a sixth sense would soon be on the prowl. But it wasn't long before my annoyance turned to anxiety. Perhaps she had slipped and lay hidden out of view. I'd better do something. Best give her a shout. It was only then I realised I didn't know her name.

Stupid not knowing her name. I should have asked but, when the moment arose, it seemed too late in the day for introductions. A few half-yodelling 'hellos' later, I realised the futility of it all. Perhaps she had found it too difficult and climbed back up to try the other branch. Perhaps she was stuck halfway down. The only sensible thing to do was to climb back the way I had come down then, finding the top of the gully, follow the route she had descended. In that way I'd cover all corners.

I climbed back into the mist by now a little out of breath. For a few moments I thought I had lost my bearings then suddenly the twisted rock loomed out of the mist and I was once again standing at the head of the twin gullies. I carefully picked my way down the left-hand branch, calling as I went. I was right. There was a lot of loose rock that could easily be disturbed in descent and I made every effort to move as carefully as possible. I eventually reached the little shelf above the bad step. If she had slipped anywhere, it was most likely she would have slipped here. I shouted again into the mist. No answer. I'd have to go keep going. Must be careful here. Keep three points of contact. Watch where you're putting your feet. One clumsy move and what might at this moment be nothing more than a sprained ankle could quite easily turn into a fractured skull.

I was virtually at the bottom of the gully when, as suddenly as it had come down, the mist started to clear. First in wisps and then, with a sudden sweep, the whole lot lifted. I had a complete view both above and below. No sign, no sound of any being. Where on earth was she? And then it dawned on me. She must have decided to push on, thinking I was ahead of her. No matter – if I hurried, I should catch her before she reached the track – a rather ridiculous game of the pursuer being chased by the pursued. I broke into a trot. A week on the hill had hardened the muscles and fine-tuned the balance. It wouldn't be long before I caught her up. I quickly reached the foot of the rake and stopped to look back at the hillside. Again, no sign. If she had tried to climb down directly, that cagoule would have stuck out like a sore thumb. Perhaps I'd taken longer to reclimb the gully than I'd thought.

It was only when I reached the head of the track that I stopped and tried to make sense of the whole thing. I had a clear view all the way down to the valley. Even if she had run like the wind she'd have still been in sight. What on earth was she up to? Some sort of game? I was beginning to think that I was the victim of a complicated practical joke. What did she say about dropping into another valley? Fun? I'd thought that rather an odd remark at the time. In fact, if you come to think of it, the whole thing seemed a bit of a set-up. She could have chosen another seat on the train. It wasn't as though it was full. And why turn up at the pub? How could I be sure what was going on? Perhaps she had planned to go home alone all along. I stopped to look at my watch. Decision time. If I got a move on, I could still catch the 4.30.

I started jogging once more. The going on the bulldozed track was easy and I soon settled into a regular rhythm. Now that my mind could slip into auto, I started thinking again. What if she had fallen and I had somehow passed her in the mist? Surely she would have called out. Anyway, the mist had lifted by then. Should I go back? Inform the authorities with all the inevitable follow-up, the knock on the door, the half-accepted explanations at home? No, she knew what she was doing. If you decide to walk in the hills alone, you accept the possible consequences. If she had got down the gully without any problem, she was bound to have been all right. I cast my mind back to the ease of movement she had shown while apparently gliding from hold to hold. More floating than climbing. No, she'd definitely be OK and anyway what was I supposed to do? Spend the rest of my life wandering aimlessly around Craig Coire nan Lochan?

I had just about reached the end of the track with the station within easy reach when I heard the mournful sound of the diesel's horn as it emerged out of the tunnel into the strath. Perhaps that was the trigger or perhaps whatever was going on in the churnings at the back of my mind eventually broke through to the surface. Of course, I'd been chasing the wrong bus. It wasn't the first sentence of that short story that was relevant. It was the title I'd given it. I suddenly saw – or, rather ruefully, heard – in my mind the quinquesyllabic phrase I had typed at the top of the page.

I sat once more on the train to Inverness. On the other side of the shared table a man in a suit opened his briefcase and took out some papers tied together with pink ribbon. I looked out of the window, watching the slopes of Craig Coire nan Lochan sliding from view. It was probably at that moment I fully understood what possibly I had known all along – that the world is divided into those who do and those who don't accept the invitation suggested by *The Half-Opened Door*.

## IF ONLY

If this particular train of events that ended so – I'm still not sure what the right word is – started anywhere, it started in a bar with those two girls who were sitting at the table next to me. They got up and I had assumed they were leaving when one turned in my direction. *Would you please guard our seats, while we have a ciggy?* The end of her sentence managed to squeeze its way through the by now closing door. Not much choice there then. They were what my soon-to-be ex-wife ('Marjory' turned out to be Michael) would have collectively called 'smart tart'. Mind you, my soon-to-be ex-wife, although indubitably smart, was also a bit envious of tarts, smart or otherwise. In any event these particular girls had enough about them to demand attention. I can still see my *Of course* sliding, disconsolately, down the now intervening glass panel.

It was a pretty stupid thing to agree to. The bar was filling up and before long stronger men than me would march in and airily dismiss my *I think those seats are taken* with an *I expect they've gone by now*. Then where would I be? But *guard*. I liked that word. It held a sense of purpose, a sense of consequence, a straightening of the shoulders, a narrowing of the eyes. Like that scene in *The Magnificent Seven* when whosit rode shotgun on the hearse. Yes, I liked *guard*.

Of course, I quickly realised that the most likely consequence of guarding was I'd be even later for my doctor's appointment than I was already. If matters did come to a head, I didn't really have time to summon even a token resistance let alone a full-length production of 'Horatius at the Bridge'. Come on, come on. How long can a ciggy take? For all I knew they could be working their way through a packet of Capstan Full Strength.

And that was another thing the doctor will say. Along with the drinking. Not that they really were doctors any more, just medical centre staff who filled in forms that sent you to other doctors who had better insurance policies. Those chaps, in the old days, they probably didn't know much, but they were much more reassuring with their *Take one of these twice a day and come back and see me if things don't improve* as they puffed on their pipes and hastily shoved the bottle of Scotch back in the medicine cupboard. Nowadays, as with everything else, it's all a game of I know, they know, I know, they know.

'You're more than ten minutes late.' The receptionist looked first at her register then at the clock on the wall. 'Do you realise how much money is wasted by people like you turning up late?'

'I'm sorry. I got held up at the bridge.'

'Bridge? What bridge? Oh, never mind. Take a seat and wait to be called.'

I sat down. Apart, I suppose, from a concoction of infection left by my precursors, the waiting room was devoid of life. Eventually a harassed mother and child scuttled through and disappeared past the desk in a flurry of ill-tempered anxiety. Then nothing until the crackle of an intercom invited me to make my way to Surgery 3.

Dr Walker looked at his watch. 'Sorry to keep you waiting. Never seem to run to time these days now we've got this internet thing. They're all over it now. Patients, I mean. First sign of a cough and they imagine they've got anything from consumption to Barrett's oesophagus. It was bad enough when they started sticking *Gray's Anatomy* on library shelves. Still, worse things happen at sea. Now then, how can I help you?'

'I've come about the tests. When I saw Mr Sterne, he said...'

'Ah, yes. Of course.' Dr Walker shuffled some papers around his desk while he collected his thoughts. 'Yes, here we are. Not too good I'm afraid. Sterne confirms what we have suspected all along. Mind you, it's not all gloom and doom.' A further shuffle. 'Yes, here we are. The latest batch of tests show it's still at a relatively early stage and these things can take time to fully develop.'

'How long? I mean how long before things develop – fully?'

Dr Walker leant back in his chair and rubbed his hand over his chin. 'Well, that rather depends on the individual. It's probably true to say, in cases like this, that God helps those that help themselves. Sensible diet, exercise, plenty of fresh air, that sort of thing. I see you've given up smoking. That's good. Don't start again and go easy on the alcohol. I would like you to make an appointment to see me in, let's say, three months' time. Meanwhile I'll have a word with Sterne to see if he can put some sort of number on it.'

As that seemed to be that, I started to gather my belongings together. 'There is one other thing, I might mention.' I stood coat half off, half on. 'I know this doesn't sound very helpful but no one yet fully understands the physical consequence of mental stress. All I'm saying, it might help in both the short and long term if you try to take it easy and find something of interest, a new hobby perhaps, to help you relax. Don't forget to make that appointment on your way out and if you have any further problems don't hesitate to give the surgery a call.'

I stood for one last moment at the door of the centre, ruffled my scarf up under my chin before stepping out into a typically raw November evening. *A new hobby.* What was that all about? *Fretwork!* The new, instant cure for all known diseases. Well, that should save the NHS a bob or two. Anyway, the whole 'it's all in the mind' malarkey is probably just gobbledegook dreamt up at some obscure American college or other. As for the *might help in both the short and the long term*, what was the phrase that crops up in the obits – *after a long/short and brave struggle against...* Which, roughly translated, means the poor sod managed to hang on a bit longer than most people expected. Odd expression, 'hanging on'; I mean hanging on to what? More like clutching at straws. Talking of which, what I need is a drink. But as I walked through the car park towards the main road, I suddenly remembered. The crucial phrase wasn't *hanging on* at all. It was *Hold on!* Coupled with the image of a child kneeling by the side of his bed. That child, now sixty-nine years old, could still see, on the wall opposite, a poem in a dark mahogany frame. It wasn't the Yanks who had stumbled on the efficacy of mind over matter. It was Rudyard bloody Kipling.

It had been more than expected that before escaping the cold of the unheated bedroom, my brother and I should spend a decent interval of time, hands clasped, eyes closed, asking the Good Lord for general forgiveness on the one hand and an easy passage through life on the other. As I could usually manage to gabble through this in a few seconds, I had to devise some other distraction to fill the unforgiving minute. It didn't take me long to realise that if, at a reasonably slow speed, I read the text conveniently laid out on the wall before me, that would more or less cover parental expectation. Over the following weeks and months, I must have inadvertently learnt the whole thing by heart and could, if requested, rip through the thirty-two lines from *keeping your head* to *being a man, my son* in around thirty seconds flat. Probably, if pushed, I could drag most of it back, even now.

No need then for expensive research, papers in learned journals or clinical trials. Copyright has fortunately expired. All that was required was a printing press and a few of the unemployed to deliver a copy to every household.

*If you can force the heart and nerve and sinew*
*To serve you long after they are gone,*
*Tum-tum-te-tum when there is nothing in you*
*Except the Will which says to them: 'Hold on!'*

Once it is generally realised that good health is only a matter of willpower the *Daily Mail*, no doubt, will take up the cudgels, requesting, nay demanding, their readers' emotional response to the conditional advice proposed by 'our country's finest poet'.

*If it hadn't been for 'IF' I would never have...*
*A magnificent monument to England's manhood...*

*Before each of our little gatherings the Chairman stands and recites Mr Kipling's wonderful poem...*

Even as a child, I had had my doubts. I mean, how could the heart, nerve and whatnot 'hold on' when they had already bolted? Much later in life, I realised it was just the inadequacy of a poet who was prepared to sacrifice sense in order to find a rhyme. A Jack and Jill moment, so to speak. I mean the last place you'd expect to find copious supplies of water is at the top of a bloody hill. And when it comes to hobnobbing with royalty and having a bad day at the gee-gees, Kipling's poem started to fall apart at the seams. But you have to make allowances. The poor lad was named after a reservoir that thought it was a lake. *Hold on?* If I was going to hold on to anything, it would be a glass of the amber liquid. As I've already mentioned, what I need is a drink.

Five years ago, I wouldn't have been seen dead in a place like this. Five years ago, I would have been standing at the bar of the King Bill adding my ten penn'orth to what we collectively regarded as native wisdom and wit. These days, I can't stand for long and the alternative to sitting by myself, Billy No-Mates, in the bar parlour of the King William IV is here at the Pink Parrot where I could pass for an occasional diner. For the Pink Parrot is not a pub but a wine bar, populated, during the day, by the young mothers who traditionally would have congregated in the terrace tea room of some fashionable department store, and, from five o'clock onwards, by those feasting on whatever blubber the latest financial boom had brought to the surface.

'Excuse me. It is, isn't it?' I looked up. The face didn't seem familiar. 'You probably don't remember me. You taught me at Shot, Shothurst Sec. Here, let me get you a drink. Scotch by the look of it.' He disappeared in the direction of the bar. I looked again carefully. No, no idea. It mustn't have taken him long to attract the attention of the bar staff as I was still rifling through a list of possibilities when he returned with what were obviously doubles.

'Hope you like malt. This one's rather special, a sixteen-year-old Jura. The Parrot was lucky to get a case. Most of it went to the Japanese. You don't mind if I join you, do you?' I had to look beyond the receding hair and the beginnings of a double chin before I could place him.

'It's Shuff, isn't it? Joey Shufflebottom.' The figure opposite smiled. Joey Shufflebottom had been one of the chosen few. Probably not Joey any more. More likely Joe rather than Joseph. 'So, what have you been doing with yourself for the last thirty years?'

Joey manoeuvred himself into a more comfortable position. 'Well I passed all the exams and my mam was quite keen that I went on to the grammar, but the old fella was dead against it. *Waste of time. Get out and get yourself some money, lad. Find yourself a proper job.* So I told them at school I wouldn't be applying. Of course, the head went ballistic. Even came round the house one evening to get me to change my mind. I thought me dad would have a real go but he just stayed quite calm and asked old Barney how much a teacher earns in a week. Barney spluttered a bit but eventually came out with a figure. For a moment or two, the old fella said nowt then gave it him straight. *I look at it this way, Mr Barnfather. I can earn that much a day dropping tarmac. Now I don't have much education but I can still reckon well enough. If you multiply that figure you mentioned by six to get my weekly wage, then by fifty for the weeks you work in a year and then by five again to cover the time spent study-ing, it looks like a tidy sum I'd be losing just to have some fancy initials*

115

*after my name. No, Mr Barnfather, our Joe will be getting a proper job, starting a week Monday.* And that was that.'

I looked at the well-cut suit, silk tie and obviously expensive shoes. 'It seems your father was right. So what exactly are you up to?'

'Finance.' He must have seen my expression of disbelief. 'Oh no, not here, not in this dump of a town. I am just down visiting my mam. I work and live in the city nowadays. Greater Northern Finance Services. You must have heard of us. We're always on the telly. Yeah, I'm doing OK – General Manager North West.' Joe twisted in his seat and raised his right hand in the direction of the bar. 'I know I wasn't much cop at English, but I usually came top in Mr Smith's maths class.'

'Well, as I said, it looks as if your father was right.'

'Not really. Dropping tarmac's a pretty shit job. Finance is the thing. There's real money in that.' Whatever response I might have made was cut short by two more doubles arriving at the table. I started to mutter some platitude about quality of life but by now Joey was in full swing. 'The whole thing's a piece of cake. We borrow the money from the bank at $x$ per cent and lend it to the punter at $y$ per cent. The gap between those two figures is our profit.'

'That's if the punters pay up.'

'Oh, they pay up all right.' He gave me a wink. 'Our bonuses depend on it.' He waved his glass in my direction. 'Mind you, the competition's hotting up these days, so we've got to keep one jump ahead of the crowd.' Joe settled more squarely in his seat and, leaning towards me, lowered his voice. 'You won't believe this, but head office's latest idea is an *interest-free* loan.'

'So what happens to the cake?'

For a moment Joey looked puzzled. 'Ah, I see what you mean. Piece of cake. No problem. In nearly every case you get an even bigger slice, if you get my meaning.' He paused for a moment to make sure I'd picked up the pun. 'Simplicity itself. It works like this. Houseowners only, mind you. They can take out a six-month loan interest-free. Maximum amount, 75 per cent of the value of their property.'

'Hang on. I don't follow this. Are you saying I could borrow thousands of pounds, put it in a savings account, earn the accrued interest, then after six months pay the original sum back?'

'Exactly.'

'So Great...'

'Greater.'

'Greater Northern Finance are going to give me several hundred pounds out of the goodness of their hearts.'

Joe nodded. 'Provided, of course, you repay before the due date.'

'And if you don't?'

'That's when the rest of the contract kicks in.'

Comprehension was now beginning to dawn. 'At, I suppose, a rate rather higher than $y$.'

'And for a minimum of twenty-four months" – sounds less than two years' – compound interest. Of course, they always believe they will pay it off, but it doesn't take long before they decide to spend a bit of it on a holiday or something, thinking to make up the difference before the six months are up. As you never tired of telling us, sir, the road to hell is paved with good intentions. Right, I must be off. Great to see you again, sir.' Joe finished his drink in one go while simultaneously reaching into an inside pocket. 'The office number's on the card. If you're ever in town and fancy a jar, give me a bell.'

*Or watch the things you gave your life to, broken.* A National Health Service based on wishful thinking, teaching children to add up so that they can inflict misery on others. It would seem that the brave new world dreamt up by the post-war Labour government had at some point taken a wrong turning.

\*

It was some little time before either Kipling or Joe recrossed my mind. Unsurprisingly, it was during the course of one of my ever-increasing bouts of insomnia. After working through the traditional sheep census routine, I would get up, go downstairs to the kitchen and make myself a drink. Invariably, depending on mood, this would be either black coffee or malt whisky, the latter if I was feeling particularly sorry for myself. And it was usually when in one of those moods that I would resurrect the latest version of The Plan.

I suppose most people have *a* plan. In some ways it's an essential part of life, better to travel hopefully sort of thing. It probably starts with the phrase *when I'm grown up*, which seems to offer a myriad of opportunity. But the trouble with being *up* is that, once there, the only other direction is *down*. Of course, you can kid yourself you've still got a future. The 'get married, acquire children and a semi on the bypass' sort of future. Been there, seen it – not, I may add, with that much success. I suppose Miranda, being bright enough to go to Cambridge and get a worthwhile job, was some sort of a tick. But set against that was her choice of husband, the insouciant Roger, who seemed to do little more than prop up the bar of the golf club in his barathea blazer and faux Guards tie. As for the soon-to-be ex-wife, probably the less said the better.

No, *the* plan, my plan, I would like to think, was of a different order to that. Over the years, of course, it had changed, from sporting glory in childhood through a variety of middle-aged ambitions, to the greater certainty shaped by diminishing opportunity. At each stage I must have recast it, burnished it, held it up to the light until I was satisfied that it was right in every particular, a chrysalis waiting to burst into the magnificent butterfly of my imagination. But no matter how many malt whiskies you consume, life like a conjuror always has a stumbling block or two up its voluminous sleeve. In my case it wasn't the commonly pleaded lack of opportunity – my current matrimonial state meant there was never a better time to make a screeching handbrake turn. No, in my case, it was money or rather the lack thereof. The Plan, as it now stood, was expensive and no matter how I did the figures, whatever trade-off I did with the soon-to-be ex-wife, there was still a considerable shortfall. And, I suppose, it was in one of those moments of self-indulgent regret, there occurred in my thoughts the unlikely combination of a Nobel Prize for Literature winner and Joey Shuff.

As must be clear by now, dear old Rudyard's advice on how to become a leading light in the Young Conservatives was not one of my picks for *The 100 Poems to Have at Your Bedside*, but there was one short section that had always seemed to have a bit more beef about it.

*If you can make one heap of all your winnings*
*And risk it on one turn of pitch-and-toss*
(And not only beef but also a touch of the Rubicon.)
*And lose, and start again at your beginnings*
*And never breathe a word about your loss*

If you cut through the injured martyr bit and assumed the risking all your winnings on *one* turn of pitch-and-toss meant something more important than losing what you had already won on the first five races, then JRK might, just might, have been on to something. A Mallory moment, to be the first man to climb Everest and probably die in the attempt or retreat to a life of an everlasting what-iffery. That, under the circumstances, might be a way forward. What was Sterne's prognosis? Three to five years? Well, if I was ever going to do something, this was the moment.

So it came about that by the most unlikely of chances Joseph Rudyard provided the method and Joey Shuff, or rather Great, sorry Greater, Northern Finance Services, provided the means.

It only took three calls. The first to my local estate agent who, sensing a quick profit, was more than happy to give me a 'ballpark' figure. The second to the local branch of Crown Entertainments Ltd to confirm my assumption that, unless I had an authorised account, all transactions were strictly cash. The last to the number on Joey's card.

'Greater Northern Finance. How can I help you?'

'Could I speak to Mr Shufflebottom please?'

'I'll see if he's available. Who shall I say's calling?'

There was a short pause followed by a rather hesitant start to an orchestral arrangement of 'Greensleeves'. The earpiece crackled, 'I'm sorry, sir, Mr Shuff...' Her voice was cut off by further cracklings and 'Oh, hello, sir. I didn't realise it was you at first. How can I help?'

'You remember when we met at the Pink Parrot, you mentioned an interest-free loan. Well, I'd like to take you up on it.'

'Are you sure? I did mention the default interest was pretty hefty, didn't I?'

'Yes, you did and yes, I'm sure.'

'OK. If you're really sure. How much for?'

'A hundred thousand.'

'Sorry, I didn't quite catch that. I thought you said 100K.'

'That's what I said. I want to borrow one hundred thousand pounds for six months, interest-free.' Silence followed. For a second I thought we'd been cut off. 'Hello, are you still there?'

'Yes, yes, I'm still here. If you're quite sure, I'll look into it. But you do understand that it's quite a rigmarole. We'll have to inspect the property first. Check your credit rating, that sort of thing. But if you could give me your full name, address and postcode, I'll start the ball rolling.'

'And there's another thing. I want the money in cash.'

'Cash? 100K in cash?'

'Yes. Pound notes. Or more precisely, fifty-pound notes.' I was rather beginning to enjoy myself.

'Right, I'll have to clear that with head office. Could you give me your mobile and I'll be in touch as soon as possible.'

*

I opened the lid. The bundles of fifty-pound notes, each held together by a neat paper band, fitted exactly the available space in my father's old leather document case. It might have been made for the job. A disembodied voice emerged through the shatterproof screen. 'Yes?' A young woman looked up at me and then at the clock on the wall. 'You'll have to be quick.' I turned the case round so the contents were visible.

'I would like to exchange this for the highest denominational chips available please.'

'Pass it through the gap.' A panel slid open and with some difficulty I squeezed the case through the aperture. The cashier opened the lid and, picking out the bundles one at a time, counted the individual notes with surprising rapidity. A seemingly never-ending flurry of Her Majesty's head. There was something about her efficiency of movement that seemed familiar. Eventually the last bundle had been counted and returned to the only remaining space. Pushing the case to one side, she looked up, first at me then the clock, her fingers drumming impatiently on the counter that separated us. 'In total, I make that one hundred thousand pounds...

*... in fifty-pound notes.* I watched Joe slowly push the final bundle across his desk. So it hadn't been that difficult, after all. Of course, Joe had made a bit of a meal of it. *'Hello sir, I've got what you wanted – one hundred thousand in fifties. I can tell you it wasn't easy. I had to pull in a few markers. There's only one small snag. You'll have to come into town to sign all the necessary papers. Would five tomorrow afternoon be OK?'* Five tomorrow afternoon would be more than OK. Pick up the money, take a taxi to the casino and Bob's – or rather two million bobs – your uncle.

It had been during the journey to the Blue Lagoon Casino that I began to have second thoughts. I've been using taxis quite a lot recently and have a good idea what the average cabbie is like. This one was different. He didn't talk for a start and when he slowed down to let a car out of a side road, I really began to panic. Perhaps he wasn't a cab driver at all. Perhaps the whole thing was a set-up. Calm down. What did the man say? If you can keep your head when all about you... Perhaps it was the thought of those about me losing theirs that did the trick. Miranda would adopt one of her *How many times have I told you?* expressions and the sight of the Sponge when he realised the inheritance was probably slipping through his fingers – *You can't be serious, one hundred thousand pounds!...*

... in fifty-pound notes?' She looked up, clearly annoyed by the delay. 'One hundred thousand pounds in fifty-pound notes. Is that right?'

I nodded. 'Sorry, I was miles away.'

The chair swivelled to allow the cashier to turn to the device behind her. Buttons were pressed and then with a machine-gun rattle a slip of paper slowly appeared. The panel slid up. 'Your receipt. One hundred thousand pounds sterling. Before completing a transaction of this size, I have to have the amount rechecked.' By this time, she was fastening up her coat and gathering up the rest of her belongings. 'If you take a seat at the bar, the manager will be with you in a moment.'

'Large malt, please. Jura, if you have it. No ice.' By now my eyes were starting to get used to the general gloom that surrounded the pools of light cast on the various gaming tables.

'Large Jura, sir, no ice.'

'Fine, keep the change.' If you're going to bet real money, you should at least play the part. But then, as I looked around, what really struck me was how drab the place looked. I mean, I wasn't expecting tiaras and white tuxedos but at least a bit of smart tart and fat old men clutching a bunch of tenners in ring-encased fingers. This lot were just like Ladbrokes on a wet Saturday afternoon. Mind you, they'd perk up a bit when I started to place my little heaps of chips on the table. I mean, even the highest of rollers would regard a hundred thousand as a serious amount of money. A couple of Juras later I moved away from the bar so I could get a closer look at the layout. The outside bets? Odd/even. Red/black. Good, it was just as I expected. Just like the illustration in Hoyle. Also, just what I needed, plenty of room in the red zone.

I had decided, win or lose, I would go out with a certain éclat. I would place my first heap of chips, say, five thousand pounds' worth, on red. This would attract immediate attention. Then in ever-increasing amounts I would fill up the remaining available space, each dwindling space neatly covered with an elegantly constructed heap of wealth. All this would be done slowly and with apparently careful thought, allowing the word to get around and the gathering to increase in direct proportion to the amount being placed. At the last, when I had the final chip left, I would pause as if undecided, before placing it on black. Then, finally satisfied, I would step back and let life's pitch and toss do its job. Proper éclat. Or did I mean élan?

A fresh round had just started. I watched the ball spinning around the rim of the wheel, first in a ferocious blur, then slowing to a tantalising bobble that threatened to settle first on to one number then another before capriciously landing on a third. Nine red. Perhaps black would be a better bet. Perhaps not. I tried to imagine how I would feel when it was my ball that was bouncing around – a man, ice axe in hand, about to make an irreversible step – now reduced to a little ball, each bounce a little slower than the last until finally it stops and the decision is made. Red, two hundred thousand pounds. Black? I wasn't sure, but fretwork wouldn't figure much on the agenda. I took a step nearer the table. I began to wonder how much I should tip the croupier.

'Excuse me, sir.' Such had been my concentration on the

job in hand that it took a moment for me to realise that the barman had left his post and was now standing beside me. 'Excuse me, sir, Mr Whitmore is ready to see you now. If you would follow me, please.' Together we crossed the room to a door marked *Private*. The barman first knocked, then opened the door before standing to one side. A figure, who I presumed was the casino manager, beckoned me in. The room, lit by a low shaded light, was in semi-darkness. On the table under the light was my money – at least, I assumed it was my money – just as I had handed it over to the cashier except for three or four notes that had been extracted and placed to one side. On the far side of the table stood a second figure who stepped forward out of the half-light. He gesticulated towards the money. 'Is this the money you left with the cashier?' The whole situation reminded me of a not-very-good B-movie.

'I suppose so. It looks like it. I started to put my hand into my inside pocket. 'I've got a receipt.'

'That'll not be necessary. Please sit down. I have a few questions I need to ask you. I am Detective Inspector Pattinson and this is Sergeant Dodds.' I turned to see a third man sitting in a corner, notebook in hand. 'Before we start, I should warn you that anything you say will be taken down in writing and may be used as evidence against you.'

'This is ridiculous. You can't be serious.'

'Quite serious, sir. In these parts we regard money-laundering as a very serious matter indeed.'

## THE GREAT ESCAPE

In my heart of hearts, I knew it was bound to happen. Come as inevitably as the dreams had come. Dreams that were so close to reality that on awakening the spasm of relief almost hurt. But dreams merely rehearse the inevitable. The only surprise was it ended not with the demanding bang on the knocker but the whimper of a badly connected front-door bell.

*It was*, she said, as she took off first her gloves then her coat while he settled down with my paper in what he knew was my chair, *time for a serious discussion*. The discussion – inquisition would be nearer the mark – followed the traditional route. Two interrogators, one hard, one soft. The first determined you face up to the consequences of your actions. *Next time she might not be able to talk his way out of it. Did he realise the inconvenience he had caused to others through,* as it was so delicately phrased, *his ill-advised behaviour? If it hadn't been for Roger using his influence with his friends at the club... Well. One shudders to think.* The other, glancing up from the paper, urged that to come to terms with reality – a phrase designed to support any argument, squash any objection – would really help in the long term. There would be people to look after you. *You know how important it is you fol-low the doctor's advice to the letter.* The short-term pain, which it was admitted was probably inevitable, would be more than requited by the larger sense of peace and well-being. *We, of course, could look after everything.* They had the necessary papers. In the end, to be fair, there was no light blinding the eyes and the lengths of rubber hose, if present, were certainly well concealed. But, in the end, they did it. They almost persuaded me it was really my fault and if I would just sign here and here... *There, that wasn't so difficult, was it?* Confession brings its own relief and not only to the confessor.

The consequent proceedings – perhaps 'procedures' would be a more appropriate word – were remarkably swift. One minute you're free to go wherever you wish, the next you're shut up in a... What's the best way to describe it? But there's no one term. Each would have his or her own vision condensed into or illuminated by a single word. For some, it might be little more than an expletive, apparently mean-ingless, yet containing between the sharp brackets of inha-lation and exhalation all the frustration that words cannot reach. Though for others, it might require more – a literary allusion or a philosophical trope. My eventual choice was 'room', on the grounds that there wasn't any. But despite their very best efforts to explain there was really no choice, I knew, *in extremis*, there was always a choice. Even the unfor-tunate Prince of Denmark (surely not the sharpest knife in the drawer) realised that. There are always options and, in this case, the simplest of these is escape.

But before you start on such a course of action the im-portant thing is to distinguish between 'escape' and 'ab-scond'. The second is only a game, no more real than pre-tending to commit suicide. That was Charlie's way. As a child at school Charlie would place his metal pencil box near the edge of the desk then shuffle about in such a manner that it would eventually overbalance and fall to the floor in an explosion of protractors and compasses, a black hole that for a moment or two sucked in all the attention he craved. But after such triumph, you still had to pick up the pieces. You could cover the confusion by some further clowning, but even Charlie, a consummate prince of self-deceit, knew the whole affair was an act, an insubstantial sham. No, whatever I did must not be Charlie's way. Escape must be finite and totally private. There must be no coming back. No patting yourself on the back. It wouldn't take much. A plan of elopement, then a choice of sanctuary, the grasping of a particular iron ring, nailed firmly on to a particular cathedral door. As for the actual escape route, now that I'm here, it wouldn't take long to get the lie of the land and, as for the bolt-hole, I had already given that matter a good deal of thought. One of the advantages of knowing it was bound to happen is that it gives you time to prepare.

The first six months would be crucial. After that I had only to be careful. Mind you, she was a pretty determined woman. She wouldn't give up easily. He, of course, would make a great show of concern, flooding social media with requests for 'sightings', but it wouldn't last long or, indeed, be long before his mind drifted towards some other project. Some other idea to make his ever elusive fortune. But she would keep going. Yes, the first six months would be crucial and a plan was needed, a plan to be kept to. Once more I ran over the sum of my thoughts. To survive would necessitate a roof and enough money for food, the odd luxury and the ever so necessary journeys.

There had been one bit of luck. Before all this, how should I put it, toing and froing had happened, the house had been sold *(des early Vic res in idyllic sit)* which, although ideally placed when originally purchased, had always been out on a limb. The *sensible thing* was to sacrifice the view and move into town *nearer the hospital. It would be stupid to have to make that long journey twice a week.* Of course, she was right. She always was. At least, she was never wrong, which is not quite the same thing.

While they made up their mind as to the final solution the hiatus between 'des res' and 'room' had been spent in a rented flat *handy for the shops and you can always ring a taxi if you have to* which meant my assets were no longer rotting away in bricks and mortar but safely stored (and gaining interest) in half a dozen medium-sized building societies. This arrangement had the double advantage of their whereabouts being known only to me and, as far as could be ascertained, free from rising damp and sagging roof beams. £20,000 per annum for five years. £100,000 all told. This back-of-an-envelope calculation suggested there was enough (and a bit over) to last what the medicos had finally predicted was a lifetime. Generally speaking, I did not have much faith in the profession – their main job seems to be separating the malingering sheep from the chronically sick goats – but, in this case, I felt they were probably right and if they proved to be wrong... Well, that bridge could be crossed on arrival.

But back to the present. Getting out would be the easy part. It was the next step or steps that would count. The key to success was to avoid detection. Rule One – keep on the move. Rule Two – don't draw attention to yourself. Rule Three – don't break Rule Two by following Rule One too assiduously. And finally Rule Four – while following Rules

One, Two and Three, leave the faintest of electronic footprints. But where? That was the question. Obviously somewhere off the beaten track. West Country, Scotland, Darkest Wales – I quite liked the idea of lurking in the polysyllabic jungle of Llanbuggyhuggery.

Eventually I decided on Scotland. Most Englishmen think of Scotland as a minor appendage stuck on the top of GB, but even the most cursory glance at a map would make you realise that it's much bigger and much more remote than you might at first think. Fortunately, most people don't look at maps. Better still, a Scottish isle – the Outer Hebrides had a certain ring about it. I'd read once there were seven hundred and eighty Scottish islands. That should be enough to be going on with. Make it up as you go along. If the aim is to confuse others, then keeping yourself guessing must be a good start. A map and a pin, that's all you need. I always liked maps, sweeping the domestic debris from the kitchen table, spreading out the chosen portion of the Ordnance Survey, trying to picture the rise and the fall of the land. Yes, I would like that, planning the next move would be a nice way to pass a long winter evening, chucking another log on the fire, pouring a more than generous malt.

Which leads to the matter of a roof over your head. Winter would be easy. There's bound to be a plethora of empty holiday cottages the locals are only too willing to let. And in the summer, he could put up in two or three different hotels. His sudden appearance and lengthy stay could be explained easily enough. *Deadline looming. Need a bit of peace and quiet to get the damned thing finished. You know what publishers are like.* Yes, he had always liked the idea of being thought of as an author admired by the discerning few – the slim volume on the booksellers' shelves – and it wasn't as though he hadn't tried. Perhaps wildlife photography would be an easier cover story. Well, certainly easier than fly-fishing. But that was all for the future – something to dream about. The immediate question was how to get out.

The simplest way was to walk out but there were a number of factors that militated against that. They were quite happy to let the inmates wander around the gardens during the day but there always seemed to be at least one of the attendants hovering in the background, keeping an eye, so to speak. No doubt, if asked, they would explain it was just for your own good, just being on hand in case they could be of any use, etc., etc. Anyway, if I disappeared during the day, the hue and cry would start within minutes.

Night-time would be ideal, but at nine o'clock they locked all the doors and although, after that time, it was possible for visitors to come and go through the main entrance, they had to be signed in and out by the night porter or whatever they called him. The downstairs windows had fancy latticework in front of them, neo-gothic apparently. But no matter how they described them, bars are still bars.

The first-floor windows looked more promising. The window in 'room' did have a small light that could be opened but it had been constructed so you could hardly get a hand let alone a body through it. However, at the end of the corridor that linked the rooms in my section there was a large sash window. Investigation had shown that it would only open a few inches at the top before it hit the buffer of solid wooden blocks that had been secured in the recess of the top runners. The bottom half had no such impediment but was securely screwed down. Not easy, but a definite possibility. With a few turns of the screw I could be out and (by now I had my face squashed against the glass pane) down what appeared to be a handily placed drainpipe. The icing on the cake was a sturdy-looking hopper that, I suppose, collected the rainfall from the adjacent roof. Once I was out of the window and on to the sill, it seemed ideally positioned to act as first a foot- and later a hand-hold to assist a descent.

But how could I lay my hands on the right tool? I could hardly ask for one and they weren't in the habit of serving the evening cup of cocoa with a selection of screwdrivers. But the funny thing is, that is exactly what they did. Along with the cup, saucer and plate was a teaspoon, the handle of which had a particularly distinctive shape. Instead of the normal rounded affair, the end had been squared off and resembled nothing more than the business end of the tool in question.

First, I established the habit of looking out of the window, explaining I liked to watch the birds fossicking about. *Just like us really*. Then when the coast was clear, inserting the spoon handle into the slot of a screw end and starting to shift it in an anti-clockwise direction. Despite their age, the screws turned relatively easily. Probably the wood was a bit rotten. Screw a bit out – screw it back. A bit further each day until they eventually came free. Then screw them in and out so they moved easily. There wouldn't be much time and it would be dark. Once more with your eyes shut – screw them out and back in again. Right, ready to go. But when? Timing was important. The ideal would be a full moon. *A wild moonlit night with clouds scudding o'er the flickering sky.* Or, to put it another way – enough light to see when you had to. Enough bad weather to keep people indoors.

*

A whistle blows. A man in a pinstripe suit lowers his newspaper and looks out of the window. Someone coughs. There is always a moment when you wonder whether it's you or the carriage next to yours that's moving, before a surge of acceleration, an increase of light, announces you are on your way. And, so, with a single bound I was free.

Of course, it hadn't been as simple as that. To start off with, there was all that business of having a temperature. I'd told them it didn't matter but they insisted on bathing my forehead and all that Florence Nightingale sort of stuff. Anyway, eventually they had left me in peace and I could put the plan into action. Dress in usual day clothes, stow pyjamas in wardrobe and, after ensuring all was silent, slide into corridor. I'd never seen the window at night-time before. It seemed to dominate proceedings, a bit like the east end of a church. Then there was the fiddling about trying to fit the end of the spoon into the slot of the screws and the moment of panic when the sash wouldn't lift up no matter how hard I tried and I thought I'd been rumbled until I realised that I hadn't undone the catch that keeps the two parts tight shut. And that wasn't the end of it. The actual climbing through the window had all been a bit of a mess. To start off with, I was taller than the frame so once out on the sill I couldn't stand upright properly. Much shuffling and dithering to get my head above the brickwork and even more dithering to pluck up courage to let the fingers ever so slowly uncurl, leave the last point of security and make the first (or possibly last) step on to the hopper. Got it. A bit of a juggle, astride the drainpipe, one foot on each side of the hopper, hands firmly entwined round the back of the downspout. Solid as rock. There is one thing you can say for the Victorians – when they built something, they built it to last. The rest was just an undignified slither before slipping into the night.

There's something odd about a town centre at three o'clock in the morning. It was not the quiet. You'd expect that. It was the shape of things. During the day the tops of the buildings stop where the sky starts, but at night it was like being in a box. Not a box, more a canyon. The walls of buildings normally truncated by the light of the sky now disappear through the glare of the street lights, rising apparently forever. Then there are the echoes, sounds you wouldn't normally hear, the clicking of heels, the soft clunk of a door being closed. When was the last time I'd been out at this hour? There was that time with Billy. (His name wasn't really Billy – it was all to do with some player in some football team or other.) We'd decided to go for a run before breakfast and left the house at some ungodly hour – funnily enough through a similar sash window – God knows why. I had spent much time and effort avoiding what I saw as a pointless exercise. *Long Broughton, the most challenging of all the school runs.* Such was its length and severity, no one was ever forced to do it. Perhaps that's why. Anyway, finished up running back through the outskirts of the town as day started to break. It was just like tonight except there were pints of milk on everyone's doorstep. We'd thought of nicking one but chickened out.

At last the corner of Station Street. All that's needed is to collect the bag and away.

The station hadn't changed much over the years. A new bookstall or, if truth be told, more or less the same bookstall in a new place, and a general removal of items that could be used as lethal weapons on a Friday night. The most obvious addition was a bank of left luggage lockers painted an almost fluorescent orange. For the umpteenth time this morning my hand had hovered over my shirt pocket to check the reassuring presence of the key. Top row, third from the right. The light wasn't good but the locker door looked slightly ajar with some sort of notice stuck on it.

*The contents of this locker have been removed pursuant to Section 7 of The Protection of People and Property Acts. The owner or owners should contact either the ticket office or the local police station where, subject to confirmation of ownership, the goods will be returned. If you have any problems, please call the following number...*

For the second time that night I feel the spasms of panic flood my thoughts. The whole thing hung on it. The whole thing was ruined. Without the bag I might as well return with my tail between my legs. I can hear her now: *How many times do I have to tell you...* and he would be no better: *Getting a bit fed up, old chap? Fancied a night on the tiles, did you?* Come on – think! A deep breath and things begin to calm. The police station would be open all night. All that has to be done is identify the contents, apologise for being a nuisance and be on my way. As long as the shaving kit was intact. That was all that mattered, the other and really important stuff is elsewhere. In fact, it might turn out for the best. Something to do. Better than just hanging about for the next two hours.

The lamp cast its familiar bluish glow, giving an odd translucence to the short flight of steps leading to the front of the police station. Right. Pause a minute. Get the story right. Left the bag in the locker the day before an appointment in London. Had to catch the early train, wasn't sure about a taxi at that hour and didn't want to carry a heavy case. That should pass muster. Appointment cancelled so collected it later.

*When did you deposit your luggage, sir?* The desk sergeant slowly got off his stool, searched under the counter and re-appeared holding a form. It could have been worse. The sergeant had probably spent his whole working life behind that and similar desks and judging by his frequent glances at the clock above the door must be nearing the end of his shift. It could have been much worse. It could have been one of those if-I'm-not-an-inspector-by-the-time-I'm-thirty-I'll-eat-my-truncheon type of smart alec. Still, better be careful. *Name?* Thought about that. May as well tell the truth. Even if they tracked my movements, they wouldn't be any the wiser. *Address?* Ditto or rather Flat 17A. *Any form of identifica-tion?* Driving licence should be in the bag. The sergeant re-turns to his list of 'enclosed items'. *Right, contents?* Apart from the licence? *Apart from the licence.* Just clothes, overnight stuff – oh, and a monogrammed shaving kit. The sergeant fingers his way down the list half talking to himself, half to anyone who might be listening. *Trainers, sweater, one shirt blue, one shirt grey. Here we are. One sponge bag, initialled.* Another glance at the clock. *That seems all in order. Could you sign here, sir?*

Find the Gents in the station. Check the shaving kit. Just for a moment... then an exhalation of breath. ID card ex-actly where I'd put it. Change clothes. Let them look for a man in red sweater and chinos. Now everything slotted into place. Travel south. Two stations go by. Alight. An anxious moment or two waiting for the metallic blinds of Securi-ty & Mail Box Inc. to be raised. Mild panic when the girl seems to have misplaced her keys. Card shown, magic num-ber tapped in. Then passbooks safely zipped into the inside pocket of anorak. Return to station. Buy ticket for Oban. All is behovely.

The northbound train for Oban draws away from the

platform. All is indeed behovely. It is always good to get away. The holiday feeling. Father, having deposited the enormous suitcase in the guard's van, fussing over Mother. My brother and I solemnly unpacking the games to while away the journey. Trains reign supreme. Buses not bad – at least you are high enough to see over hedges. That most despicable form of transport – the car... there seems no word to describe it. But behovely it is not. Where did that word come from? Some vestige of enforced worship, no doubt.

The ferry leaves the quayside with remarkable skill and the minimum of fuss. Last look at departing land. People waving. People waving back. In the sound it is quite calm, but now we have rounded the point we meet the full force of the ocean. Late autumn and the Atlantic's revving up for winter. There aren't many passengers on board and the upper deck saloon's nearly empty. Sitting on one of the cushioned benches that ran the width of the cabin was a curious experience. The pitch and roll of the boat meant that at any given moment the view to one side was of a limitless sky. To the other, a grey foam-splintered wall of sea. The whole place seemed permeated with the smell of fried food. Being sick in public would be embarrassing. Better forsake the warmth and go on deck. Even fewer people here. A young mother, with two small children, anxiously trying to sponge the mark on her coat where one of them, the little boy probably, judging by the colour of his face, had been unable to keep it down any longer. The husband, no doubt, enjoying a drink below, chatting up the barmaid. Telling a story to his captive audience of how to avoid being seasick. *If in doubt, my dear, repair to the bar and have a couple of stiff ones. When going gets rough, lurching Stomach thinks it's being poisoned. Asks Brain to assess situation. Brain detects presence of copious quantities of alcohol. Sends message. 'No problem, Stomach. Silly bugger's pissed again.' Stomach subsides.* Barmaid smiles politely. It sounds all very good in theory. It's getting cold out here. May as well give it a go.

The bar wasn't quite right. Couldn't put a finger on it but there was something that was definitely wrong. First of all, there was that business with Dave or rather without Dave, if you see what I mean. It was definitely Dave. Same fair, tightly cropped hair. Same set of the shoulders, same louche way of sitting with one arm around the back of a neighbouring chair. What on earth was he doing on my boat? No property to develop where we were going. *Dave, what the hell are you doing here?* The man turned with that polite smile of non-recognition. *Sorry, should I know you?* And then the barmaid with dark hair who once must have been quite pretty keeps asking if everything is all right, reassuring me that it was all for the best. And everyone else is talking in German. At least it sounded like German.

Eventually the boat's engine changed its beat and started to slow down, suggesting we must be near land. Back on deck for the view – that was the answer. And what a view. And what a fool to waste all that time below when I could have been on deck looking at this. As we swung from the open sea and towards the harbour, a way had to be picked through a cluster of small islands, some inhabited by the odd whitewashed cottage, others desolate, home only to the birds of these parts, fulmars, guillemots, kittiwakes, perched on ledges, and above them the gannets, patrolling the airways, ready to swoop. One such circled above the boat, quartering the sea, until without warning, wings folded, it arrowed into the swell. For a moment the centre of attention as eyes strained to see if it emerged triumphant – then suddenly forgotten when the full view of the island, my island, came into sight.

There it lay, a cluster of buildings, walls washed in a palette of colours, grouped around those staples of civilisation, the church and the licensed hotel. Slowly, you realise the whole village is contained within the protective arms of the hill that rose steeply behind it, its summit calmly gazing on all it beheld. If behovely has a superlative form, then this must be it.

Then it happened. It's not easy to tell *how* it happened. Things happen you are unable to explain. At an inquest a dozen onlookers might well have given a dozen different explanations, a variety of views. One view is it might have been my attention was distracted by Dave, if it was Dave, trying to say cheerio. Another that the deck was too slippery. Possibly a malt too many. More probably, turned too quickly and momentarily lost balance. Should have just stood still for a second, let the equilibrium return. That's what the consultant would have advised. But grabbed at the rail that shuts off the gangplank. Left shoulder bouncing awkwardly off some piece of the superstructure and then feet gone and sliding down the side of the boat into the sea.

*

It's not that cold after all. The propeller. Must avoid the propeller. Kick. That's it. Kick against the side of the boat and kick hard. Then swim, swim for your life. The swell rose and fell allowing glimpses of formless shapes. Was that a fishing boat? The two hooded figures, crouched in expectation, could be local fishermen. The swell rose and fell and they were gone. Never mind, someone must have seen. Be all right. Keep swimming. Keep head above water. Someone will see. Quite warm really. Something to do with the Gulf Stream? No that was not quite right. It had another name. It doesn't matter. Keep swimming. As the swell dropped into a trough, there was a lump of something, covered in foul-smelling seaweed and mercy upon mercy it's a buoy, a buoy with a mooring ring. One stroke and a grab. That's all there is to it. Get your fingers around the salt-pitted circle of iron and you're safe. One, p'raps two strokes, and hang on. No, two, three and... that's it. Hang on. Hang on for grim death. But the sea rose and fell, pulling and pushing at the weakening clutch. Fingers sliding, then fingers slowly uncurling one by one until with what was a feeling of immense relief he slid into the dark vast. The water was not as cold as he had imagined. Schoolboy memories of the North Atlantic Drift passed through his mind. But he couldn't be sure. He couldn't be sure of anything any more.

## CODA

Ian Johnson waited patiently, as Lot 20, a rather nice Japanese screen inlaid with jade, was removed from the viewing stage. As its size and weight required both of the porters and a good bit of toing and froing, it gave him time to have a proper look across the room. Most of the old faithful, of course, but two or three faces that he only half recognised. London boys probably. The screen had done rather better than he'd thought. Ian had a feeling in his bones that this could be a good day.

He had inherited the long-established McFetrich & Co, Estate Agents and Surveyors from his uncle and, at the time, the attached sale room had been just that. A repository for house clearances and odd bits of outdated bric-a-brac. But Ian had had other ideas. Five years in the West End had taught him a good deal about fine and decorative art and he was determined that McFetrich & Co should, in time, become a similar centre of excellence in the north. He had noticed that changes in working practices meant that the wealthy no longer clung to the cities but were moving out to small, attractive and fairly prosperous market towns like his. Farms, no longer profitable, labourers' cottages and a variety of outbuildings had been extensively and elegantly converted and awaited occupants who required furnishings to match.

But Ian also knew fashions change so he continued to offer his services when it came to sweeping up local mortal remains, and on the third Thursday of each month he returned to the firm's roots and sold, or tried to sell, a selection of outsized wardrobes, redundant encyclopaedias and ever so slightly chipped china cats. But it wasn't all philanthropy. Occasionally, among the mouldering mahogany and feline gewgaws, something of value would turn up which would be discreetly moved to the more prosperous arm of the business. There was a time when this might have included the likes of a grandfather clock but people are savvier nowadays. In this trade, as in so many others, the internet had become a double-edged sword. Nevertheless, it was one such house clearance that had produced Lot 21. Among the effects of the deceased was a fairly extensive library. Quite a lot of poetry and Renaissance drama, books on cricket and British mountaineering, the usual run of novels, biographies and collections of short stories. Bibliophilia was not really Ian's thing but even his untrained eye could see four or five items that seemed to stand out from the rest. Several telephone calls confirmed his suspicions. Two should command four figures and a couple at least wash their face.

Over time, Ian had learnt that a job lot sold better in threes. Why this was he had no real idea. Perhaps people thought they were getting value for money, perhaps some innate superstition was at work. He had little trouble deciding on two of the three books but the third choice was more problematic. Common sense dictated one of the also-rans as the makeweight. But there are times when gut instinct is better than common sense. So, for the third, he added a new but beautifully bound collection of what appeared to be nine short stories. When it came to the contents, it all seemed rather odd. There was what appeared to be a rather enigmatic overall title but no editorial explanation of why the stories had been chosen or, indeed, any indication of the identity of the individual authors. It was a bit of a punt but over the years Ian had found that what appealed to him usually appealed to his clientele. There are plenty of people who judge a book by its cover and it would make a handsome addition to anyone's bookcase.

*Ladies and gentlemen, I apologise for the delay. Lot 21.*

The years had taught Ian how to work a room. He knew how to use his head as well as the hammer and prided himself he could see who was really interested and who was not. He sensed when he might encourage the competitive nature of the bidders and when not to prolong matters unnecessarily. So who was showing interest in Lot 21? Certainly Smithson, as usual, was up for it, and the strangers – they hadn't bid on anything yet. They must have made the journey for something. And then there was a rather attractive dark-haired woman who had slipped through a left-open door just as the lot had been called. Yes, she certainly seemed interested.

*Lot 21, ladies and gentlemen. A small selection of books, ex-libris of a former resident of the Autumn Leaves Nursing Home. Each is of interest in its own right but at the request of the executors they are being sold as one lot. The first now being shown to the room by Jason is* The Children's Book of Rhyme and Proverb, *published in 1880 by J Dodd & Son of Edinburgh, compiled by Elizabeth Jane Nelson and illustrated by her brother and Royal Academician, J. Tarquin Robert-*

*son. Of particular interest is an inscription on the flyleaf of birthday greetings 'From Granny Nelson to Jack', which would suggest the book was a gift from the author to one of her grandchildren. The book is still in very good, near fine condition, which I'm sure you'd agree, given its provenance –* Ian paused and removed his spectacles to allow his audience to recall memories of overzealous crayoning – *is quite remarkable.*

*The second is a much sought-after first edition of* Scrambles Amongst the Alps *by Edward Whymper and signed by the author. This is the true first edition published in 1872 by John Murray of which only 1245 copies were printed. Again, this book, as you can see, Jason please –* the porter on cue holds the book up for general inspection – *is in near fine condition.*

*The final book in this collection of three has neither the age nor provenance of its predecessors but is not without interest. A collection of nine unattributed short stories printed and bound in Moroccan goatskin by the House of van Brougen. Both spine and cover are blind- and gold-tooled. Internally, it is handsewn with marbled endpapers. A handsome and probably unique example of the bookbinder's craft.*

*To start proceedings, I have a phone bid of fifteen hundred pounds. Sixteen hundred. Seventeen. Two thousand in the room.* The woman by the door. She hasn't put a bid in but is still clearly interested. Probably wise. No sense in pushing it up at this stage. At two five the pros had picked off the amateurs and at three thousand Smithson must have reached his client's limit. Ian glanced towards the door. Rapt attention but nothing more. At three seven Ian looked enquiringly at his assistant, who was manning the phone. The assistant shook his head. One of the strangers took off his glasses and put his catalogue in his briefcase. If she is going to make a move, this is the moment. Those two clearly aren't going to bid against each other. Whatever the deal, it'll be decided on the train home.

*Three thousand seven hundred I'm bid. The bid is with you, sir.* Ian looked pointedly towards the back of the room. *Three eight am I bid?* Ian switched his attention back to the door to find to his surprise that the chair was empty and the woman had gone. Well, he'd got that wrong, all right. *The bid is still with you, sir. For the last time, then, at three thousand seven hundred pounds.*

The auctioneer paused as convention demanded. *At three thousand seven hundred pounds, sold to the gentleman at the back of the room. Number, sir?* A man wearing a tweed suit held up his card. *143? Thank you very much, sir.*

*We move on to Lot 22, a pair of occasional tables, attributed to Hepplewhite...*

## Acknowledgements

A version of 'The Grammar School Master' appeared in *Mickey Braddock's Works Do* (Millrace, 1999). 'Anabasis' was first published in *Confingo* magazine (Spring, 2020).